Holt
Middle School Math

Homework and Practice
Teacher's Edition
Course 3

HOLT, RINEHART AND WINSTON

A Harcourt Education Company

Austin • Orlando • Chicago • New York • Toronto • London • San Diego

ISBN 0-03-066207-9

6 7 8 9   082   09 08 07 06 05

CONTENTS

Holt Middle School Math

CONTENTS, *CONTINUED*

Holt Middle School Math

Homework and Practice
LESSON 1-1 *Variables and Expressions*

Evaluate each expression for the given value of the variable.

1. $5x - 3$ for $x = 4$

_____ 17

2. $23 - b$ for $b = 16$

_____ 7

3. $\frac{1}{2}y$ for $y = 22$

_____ 11

4. $19 - 3x$ for $x = 6$

_____ 1

5. $7b - 9$ for $b = 9$

_____ 54

6. $8.6 + 9y$ for $y = 7$

_____ 71.6

7. $78 - 14k$ for $k = 5$

_____ 8

8. $9(a + 3)$ for $a = 6$

_____ 81

Evaluate each expression for the given value of the variables.

9. $3x + y$ for $x = 6$ and $y = 9$

_____ 27

10. $5a - b$ for $a = 6$ and $b = 8$

_____ 22

11. $7m - 8n$ for $m = 10$ and $n = 7$

_____ 14

12. $7r + 6s$ for $r = 12$ and $s = 14$

_____ 168

13. $10(x - y)$ for $x = 14$ and $y = 8$

_____ 60

14. $m(18 - x)$ for $m = 9$ and $x = 6$

_____ 108

A caterer determines $\frac{1}{4}$ pound of roast beef is needed to serve each guest at a party. How many pounds of roast beef are needed for each number of guests?

15. 8 guests

_____ 2 lb

16. 12 guests

_____ 3 lb

17. 18 guests

_____ $4\frac{1}{2}$ lb

18. 25 guests

_____ $6\frac{1}{4}$ lb

Holt Middle School Math

LESSON
1-2 # Homework and Practice
Writing Algebraic Expressions

Write an expression for each word phrase.

1. a number *x* divided by 7

$$\frac{x}{7}$$

2. the sum of 10 and a number *n*

$$10 + n$$

3. a number *b* decreased by 14

$$b - 14$$

4. the product of a number *x* and 8

$$8x$$

5. 12 times the difference of a number *r* and 7

$$12(r - 7)$$

6. 11 minus the product of 5 and a number *k*

$$11 - 5k$$

7. a. Grace wants to divide the job of writing *x* invitations to the party equally among 4 committee members. Write an expression to determine the number of invitations she will have each committee member write.

$$\frac{x}{4}$$

b. If Grace has 220 invitations for the committee members to write, how many will she have each member write?

55 invitations

Write an algebraic expression and use it to evaluate each word problem.

8. Arturo purchased a package of 50 blank CDs. After he used *x* CDs, he had *x* less than 50 CDs remaining. How many CDs did he have left after using 31 CDs?

19 CDs

9. At the grocery store, Henry bought *c* pounds of cashews for $4.99 per pound. If he buys 2 pounds, how much will they cost?

$9.98

Holt Middle School Math

Name _____ Date _____ Class _____

Homework and Practice
Solving Equations by Adding or Subtracting

Determine which value is a solution of the equation.

1. $x - 8 = 14$; $x = 6, 20,$ or 22

_____ $x = 22$ _____

2. $8 + a = 19$; $a = 7, 11,$ or 27

_____ $a = 11$ _____

3. $y - 14 = 22$; $y = 8, 12,$ or 36

_____ $y = 36$ _____

4. $d + 17 = 52$; $d = 25, 35,$ or 69

_____ $d = 35$ _____

Solve.

5. $m - 9 = 14$

_____ $m = 23$ _____

6. $7 + x = 16$

_____ $x = 9$ _____

7. $k + 12 = 31$

_____ $k = 19$ _____

8. $y - 14 = 46$

_____ $y = 60$ _____

9. $13 + r = 29$

_____ $r = 16$ _____

10. $17 + t = 19$

_____ $t = 2$ _____

11. $b + 39 = 57$

_____ $b = 18$ _____

12. $p + 27 = 27$

_____ $p = 0$ _____

13. $0 = w - 45$

_____ $w = 45$ _____

14. $8.7 + s = 12.1$

_____ $s = 3.4$ _____

15. $x - 3.7 = 0.8$

_____ $x = 4.5$ _____

16. $n - 3.41 = 5.40$

_____ $n = 8.81$ _____

17. The school library is combining books from two storage units into a newly designed area for the library. The first original unit held 186 books and the second unit had 307 books. Write and solve an equation to find the number of books in the new area of the library.

_____ $186 + 307 = b$; $b = 493$ _____

18. Amelia wanted to buy a new computer and printer which had a total cost of $1099.95. She had saved $389.85 for her purchase. How much more does she need to save to buy the computer and printer she wants?

_____ $389.85 + x = 1099.95$; $x = 710.10$ _____

Holt Middle School Math

Name _____ Date _____ Class _____

Homework and Practice
Solving Equations by Multiplying and Dividing

Solve.

1. $7n = 49$

$\underline{\qquad n = 7 \qquad}$

2. $6w = 48$

$\underline{\qquad w = 8 \qquad}$

3. $3a = 39$

$\underline{\qquad a = 13 \qquad}$

4. $\frac{b}{5} = 10$

$\underline{\qquad b = 50 \qquad}$

5. $\frac{x}{7} = 13$

$\underline{\qquad x = 91 \qquad}$

6. $\frac{c}{24} = 6$

$\underline{\qquad c = 144 \qquad}$

7. $12n = 96$

$\underline{\qquad n = 8 \qquad}$

8. $57 = 3k$

$\underline{\qquad 19 = k \qquad}$

9. $22x = 176$

$\underline{\qquad x = 8 \qquad}$

10. $\frac{w}{22} = 17$

$\underline{\qquad w = 374 \qquad}$

11. $\frac{h}{16} = 16$

$\underline{\qquad h = 256 \qquad}$

12. $13 = \frac{t}{33}$

$\underline{\qquad t = 429 \qquad}$

13. $572 = 26m$

$\underline{\qquad m = 22 \qquad}$

14. $\frac{x}{24} = 18$

$\underline{\qquad x = 432 \qquad}$

15. $46v = 828$

$\underline{\qquad v = 18 \qquad}$

16. $2x + 3 = 19$

$\underline{\qquad x = 8 \qquad}$

17. $\frac{r}{2} + 7 = 14$

$\underline{\qquad r = 14 \qquad}$

18. $3 = 4s - 5$

$\underline{\qquad s = 2 \qquad}$

19. Ashley saves \$32 from her weekly paycheck for her college education. This is $\frac{1}{5}$ of her weekly salary. How much does she earn each week? Write and solve an equation to determine the amount Ashley earns each week.

$\frac{c}{5} = 32; \ c = 160$

20. Hunter bought a package of 24 pencils for \$3.12. Write and solve an equation to determine the cost of each pencil in the package.

$24p = 3.12; \ p = 0.13$

Holt Middle School Math

Name _____ Date _____ Class _____

Homework and Practice
Solving Simple Inequalities

Use <, >, or = to compare each inequality.

1. $8 + 13$ $\boxed{>}$ 20

2. 23 $\boxed{>}$ $3(7)$

3. $28 - 9$ $\boxed{>}$ 18

4. 67 $\boxed{<}$ $9(8)$

5. $52 - 37$ $\boxed{=}$ 15

6. 78 $\boxed{>}$ $12(6)$

Solve and graph each inequality.

7. $x + 3 > 7$

$\underline{\qquad x > 4 \qquad}$

8. $y - 5 \le 1$

$\underline{\qquad y \le 6 \qquad}$

9. $4n \ge 20$

$\underline{\qquad n \ge 5 \qquad}$

10. $h - 1 \ge 6$

$\underline{\qquad h \ge 7 \qquad}$

11. $\frac{x}{5} < 3$

$\underline{\qquad x < 15 \qquad}$

12. $\frac{t}{3} \ge 4$

$\underline{\qquad t \ge 12 \qquad}$

13. $9d > 45$

$\underline{\qquad d > 5 \qquad}$

14. $17 + m < 23$

$\underline{\qquad m < 6 \qquad}$

15. $128 \ge 16x$

$\underline{\qquad x \le 8 \qquad}$

16. Philippe wants to drink at least 72 ounces of water every day while at work. He works 6 hours a day. How many ounces of water must Philippe drink each hour? Write and solve an inequality to answer the question.

$\underline{6w \ge 72; \; w \ge 12}$

17. Glynn's car has a 18 gallon gas tank. He travels 450 miles. What is the least miles per gallon Glynn's car will get on this trip? Write and solve an inequality to answer the question.

$\underline{18x \ge 450; \; x \ge 25}$

Holt Middle School Math

Name _____ Date _____ Class _____

Homework and Practice
1-6 *Combining Like Terms*

Combine like terms.

1. $11b + 6b$

$17b$

2. $9m - 3m$

$6m$

3. $5x + 8x + 7$

$13x + 7$

4. $8w + 9x + 7w$

$15w + 9x$

5. $13r + 10r - 8t$

$23r - 8t$

6. $9g + 4m - 8g$

$g + 4m$

7. $12b + 14p - 7$

$12b + 14p - 7$

8. $7a + 11a - a$

$17a$

9. $15 + 3x - 9 + 8x$

$6 + 11x$

10. $6x + y + x + 9y$

$7x + 10y$

11. $8m + 14 + 7m - 11$

$15m + 3$

12. $13x - 4 - 12x + 9$

$x + 5$

Simplify.

13. $5(x + 4) - 7$

$5x + 13$

14. $9(6 + y) + 3y$

$54 + 12y$

15. $6(7 + 2a) - 8a$

$42 + 4a$

Solve.

16. $5r + 2r = 21$

$r = 3$

17. $15t - 9t = 54$

$t = 9$

18. $6x + 8x = 42$

$x = 3$

19. Janelle has *d* dimes and *n* nickels. Her sister has 5 times as many dimes and 6 times as many nickels as Janelle has. Write the sum of the number of coins they have, and then combine like terms.

$d + n + 5d + 6n; \; 6d + 7n$

20. If Janelle has 9 dimes and 18 nickels, how many total coins do Janelle and her sister have?

180 coins

Holt Middle School Math

Homework and Practice
LESSON 1-7 *Ordered Pairs*

Determine whether each ordered pair is a solution of $y = 5 + 3x$.

1. (1, 8)

_____yes_____

2. (3, 7)

_____no_____

3. (2, 10)

_____no_____

4. (0, 5)

_____yes_____

Determine whether each ordered pair is a solution of $y = 4x - 1$.

5. (0, 1)

_____no_____

6. (1, 3)

_____yes_____

7. (3, 11)

_____yes_____

8. (5, 19)

_____yes_____

Use the given values to complete the table of solutions.

9. $y = x + 4$ for $x = 0, 1, 2, 3, 4$

x	x + 4	y	(x, y)
0	0 + 4	4	(0, 4)
1	1 + 4	5	(1, 5)
2	2 + 4	6	(2, 6)
3	3 + 4	7	(3, 7)
4	4 + 4	8	(4, 8)

10. $y = 2x + 3$ for $x = 0, 1, 3, 5, 7$

x	2x + 3	y	(x, y)
0	2(0) + 3	3	(0, 3)
1	2(1) + 3	5	(1, 5)
3	2(3) + 3	9	(3, 9)
5	2(5) + 3	13	(5, 13)
7	2(7) + 3	17	(7, 17)

11. $y = 4x - 1$ for $x = 1, 2, 4, 5, 8$

x	4x − 1	y	(x, y)
1	4(1) − 1	3	(1, 3)
2	4(2) − 1	7	(2, 7)
4	4(4) − 1	15	(4, 15)
5	4(5) − 1	19	(5, 19)
8	4(8) − 1	31	(8, 31)

12. $y = 5x + 2$ for $x = 0, 2, 4, 6, 8$

x	5x + 2	y	(x, y)
0	5(0) + 2	2	(0, 2)
2	5(2) + 2	12	(2, 12)
4	5(4) + 2	22	(4, 22)
6	5(6) + 2	32	(6, 32)
8	5(8) + 2	42	(8, 42)

13. Mrs. Frank had 150 customers when she began her delivery route. Each month she adds 5 new customers. The equation that gives the total number of customers, t, in her route is $t = 150 + 5m$, where m is the number of months since she began the route. How many customers will Mrs. Frank have after 12 months?

210

Holt Middle School Math

LESSON 1-8

Homework and Practice
Graphing on a Coordinate Plane

Give the coordinates of each point.

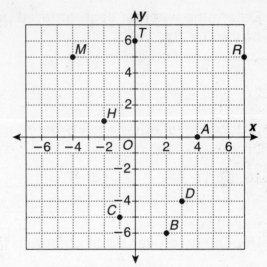

1. A

___(4, 0)___

2. D

___(3, −4)___

3. H

___(−2, 1)___

4. C

___(−1, −5)___

5. B

___(2, −6)___

6. T

___(0, 6)___

7. M

___(−4, 5)___

8. R

___(7, 5)___

Graph each point on a coordinate plane. Label points *A–F*.

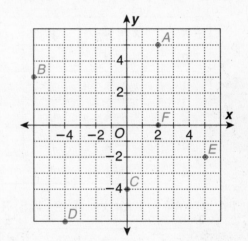

9. A(3, 5)

10. B(−6, 3)

11. C(0, −4)

12. D(−4, −6)

13. E(5, −2)

14. F(2, 0)

Complete the table of ordered pairs. Graph the equation on a coordinate plane.

15. $y = 2x$

x	x	y	(x, y)
1	(1)	2	(1, 2)
2	(2)	4	(2, 4)
3	(3)	6	(3, 6)

16. A doctor sees 4 patients each hour. Use the equation $y = 4x$, where the *y*-value represents the many patients that the doctor may see in *x* hours. Graph, if necessary. How many patients will the doctor see in a 5-hour day?

___20___

Holt Middle School Math

LESSON 1-9

Homework and Practice
Interpreting Graphs and Tables

The table gives the prices of three different stocks over the first few hours of trading. Tell which stock corresponds to each situation described below.

Time	9:30	10:30	11:30	12:30	1:30
Stock 1	$26.50	$26.00	$25.00	$24.00	$22.50
Stock 2	$38.25	$36.50	$39.75	$37.25	$41.00
Stock 3	$55.00	$55.25	$55.50	$56.00	$57.00

1. A stock opens and rises steadily over the first few hours of trading.

Stock 3 _____

2. A stock opens and declines steadily over the first few hours of trading.

Stock 1 _____

Tell which graph corresponds to each situation in Exercises 1–2.

3.

Exercise 2 (Stock 1)

4.

Exercise 1 (Stock 3)

5. Create a graph that illustrates the hours students spent studying for exams.

Student	Number of Hours Studying for Exams
Samantha	3 hours
Seth	3.5 hours
Simon	4 hours
Susan	2.5 hours

Number of Hours Studying for Exams

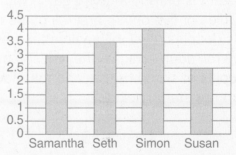

Holt Middle School Math

LESSON 2-1 Homework and Practice
Adding Integers

Use a number line to find the sum.

1. $2 + 3$

5

2. $-5 + 3$

−2

Add.

3. $-6 + 15$
9

4. $-28 + (-7)$
−35

5. $31 + (-19)$
12

6. $-34 + 21$
−13

Evaluate each expression for the given value of the variables.

7. $a + 9$ for $a = 5$
14

8. $x + 7$ for $x = 8$
15

9. $y + 6$ for $y = 13$
19

10. $-5 + r$ for $r = -7$
−12

11. $-9 + w$ for $w = -12$
−21

12. $m + 8$ for $m = -11$
−3

13. $-6 + k$ for $k = -9$
−15

14. $t + (-5)$ for $t = -8$
−13

15. $b + (-7)$ for $b = -7$
−14

16. $-11 + x$ for $x = 15$
4

17. $g + (-15)$ for $g = 15$
0

18. $-16 + j$ for $j = -18$
−34

19. The music club had 328 members. This year 103 new members joined. How many members does the music club have now?

431 members

20. Rosetta is playing a board game with her friends. She rolls doubles of five on her first roll of the number cubes. If a player rolls doubles, they roll again after moving forward. However if they roll doubles again they must move backwards. Rosetta rolls doubles of six on her second roll. How many spaces is Rosetta from her starting place?

2 back

Holt Middle School Math

Name _____ Date _____ Class _____

Homework and Practice
Subtracting Integers

Subtract.

1. 9 − 3

6

2. 12 − 4

8

3. 9 − 16

−7

4. 19 − 12

7

5. 7 − 15

−8

6. 18 − 4

14

7. −8 − 12

−20

8. −11 − 14

−25

9. 25 − 49

−24

10. 18 − 36

−18

11. −101 − 52

−153

12. −76 − (−12)

−64

Evaluate each expression for the given value of the variables.

13. $a − 10$ for $a = 7$

−3

14. $x − 13$ for $x = 20$

7

15. $17 − y$ for $y = 6$

11

16. $15 + b$ for $b = −9$

6

17. $14 − t$ for $t = −18$

32

18. $d − 24$ for $d = −17$

−41

19. $−16 − w$ for $w = −15$

−1

20. $−10 − r$ for $r = −22$

12

21. $−14 − g$ for $g = −19$

5

22. $x − (−18)$ for $x = −25$

−7

23. $y − (−14)$ for $y = −14$

0

24. $n − (−17)$ for $n = 21$

38

25. The largest island in the world is Greenland with an area of 839,999 square miles. The second largest island is New Guinea with an area of 316,615 square miles. What is the difference in the areas of the two islands?

523,384 square miles

26. Justin weighed 223 pounds and lost 45 pounds. What is Justin's new weight?

178 pounds

Holt Middle School Math

Name _____ Date _____ Class _____

Homework and Practice
Multiplying and Dividing Integers

Multiply or divide.

1. 7×9

___63___

2. $\frac{-21}{3}$

___−7___

3. -9×5

___−45___

4. $\frac{28}{-7}$

___−4___

5. $\frac{-42}{-6}$

___7___

6. $-11(-8)$

___88___

7. $\frac{-56}{-8}$

___7___

8. $4(-13)$

___−52___

Simplify.

9. $-6(4 + 5)$

___−54___

10. $9(10 - 3)$

___63___

11. $-7(13 - 4)$

___−63___

12. $8(17 - 11)$

___48___

13. $14(-5 + 3)$

___−28___

14. $-10(5 - 14)$

___90___

15. $11(-15 + 9)$

___−66___

16. $-12(-7 - 3)$

___120___

Complete the table for the equation $y = 2x - 3$.
Then plot the points on the coordinate plane.

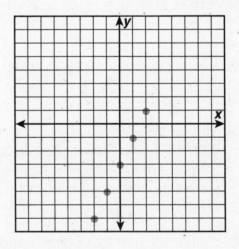

	x	2x − 3	y	(x, y)
17.	2	2(2) − 3	1	(2, 1)
18.	1	2(1) − 3	−1	(1, −1)
19.	0	2(0) − 3	−3	(0, −3)
20.	−1	2(−1) − 3	−5	(−1, −5)
21.	−2	2(−2) − 3	−7	(−2, −7)

22. Mr. Sweeney's stock portfolio lost $125 for 3 consecutive days.
What was the total dollar amount the stock lost over the 3 days?

___lost $375___

23. The temperature was −2, −3, 1, and −4 on four consecutive
days. What was the average temperature for those days?

___−2___

Holt Middle School Math

LESSON 2-4 Homework and Practice
Solving Equations Containing Integers

Solve.

1. $x + 8 = 3$

      $x = -5$

2. $y - 4 = 9$

      $x = 13$

3. $7w = 35$

      $w = 5$

4. $\dfrac{n}{-2} = 8$

      $n = -16$

5. $-8 + t = -6$

      $t = 2$

6. $\dfrac{a}{-6} = 7$

      $a = -42$

7. $-9 + k = -15$

      $k = -6$

8. $-9d = 36$

      $d = -4$

9. $c - 8 = -17$

      $c = -9$

10. $\dfrac{m}{7} = 8$

      $m = 56$

11. $-8 + b = -11$

      $b = -3$

12. $x - 19 = 19$

      $x = 38$

13. $-5x = 65$

      $x = -13$

14. $\dfrac{r}{-6} = -4$

      $r = 24$

15. $h - 17 = -12$

      $h = 5$

16. $\dfrac{x}{-6} = -6$

      $x = 36$

17. $s - 15 = -15$

      $s = 0$

18. $-64 = -8v$

      $8 = v$

19. Austin High School had an enrollment of 1,428 students. In May, they graduated 418 students. How many students are still enrolled in the school?

1,010 students

20. Mr. Otten saved $32 each week for 26 weeks. How much did he save in that time?

$832

Holt Middle School Math

Name _____ Date _____ Class _____

Homework and Practice

Solving Inequalities Containing Integers

Solve.

1. $x + 5 < 13$ **2.** $6y < -36$ **3.** $\frac{w}{-4} \geq -8$ **4.** $t - 9 > -12$

___$x < 8$___   ___$y < -6$___   ___$w \leq 32$___   ___$t > -3$___

5. $x + (-8) > 16$ **6.** $\frac{a}{8} \geq -7$ **7.** $b - (-13) < -5$ **8.** $-7r \geq -49$

___$x > 24$___   ___$a \geq -56$___   ___$b < -18$___   ___$r \leq 7$___

Solve and graph.

9. $17 + x > 13$

___$x > -4$___

10. $\frac{w}{-3} \geq -4$

___$w \leq 12$___

11. $t + (-12) \leq -7$

___$t \leq 5$___

12. $-11y < 33$

___$y > -3$___

Write an inequality for each of the following.

13. A number increased by negative fifteen is less than twenty-eight.

___$x + (-15) < 28$___

14. A number multiplied by sixteen is less than or equal to negative thirty.

___$16x \leq -30$___

15. A number divided by twelve is greater than or equal to negative thirty-four.

___$\frac{x}{12} \geq -34$___

16. A number decreased by forty-two is greater than thirty-seven.

___$x - 42 > 37$___

Holt Middle School Math

Name _____ Date _____ Class _____

Homework and Practice
Exponents

Write using exponents.

1. $8 \times 8 \times 8 \times 8 \times$
$8 \times 8 \times 8$

         8^7

2. $(-5) \times (-5) \times$
$(-5) \times (-5)$

    $(-5)^4$

3. $9 \times 9 \times 9 \times$
$9 \times 9 \times 9$

      9^6

Evaluate.

4. 10^4

   $10,000$

5. $(-4)^3$

   -64

6. $(-6)^2$

   36

7. 9^2

   81

8. 14^2

   196

9. $(-8)^2$

   64

10. $(-12)^2$

   144

11. $(-3)^4$

   81

Simplify.

12. $3^3 - 15$

   12

13. $(-4)^4 + 7$

   263

14. $7^2 - 2^5$

   17

15. $78 - 6^2$

   42

16. $11^2 - 3^4 + 3$

   43

17. $16 - 3^3 \times 4$

   -92

18. $6^2 + 10 \times 2^4$

   196

19. $-3\,(4^3 + 9^2)$

   -435

Evaluate for the given value of the variable.

20. x^3 for $x = -3$

   -27

21. $6y^2$ for $y = 4$

   96

22. $w^4 - 17$ for $w = 3$

   64

23. Write an expression for eight times a number used as a factor four times.

   $8x^4$

24. If the length of a side of a regular cube is 12 cm, find its volume.
(Hint: $V = l^3$).

   1728 cm^3

Holt Middle School Math

Homework and Practice

LESSON
2-7   *Properties of Exponents*

Multiply. Write the product as one power.

1. $10^6 \times 10^9$

   10^{15}

2. $a^8 \times a^6$

   a^{14}

3. $15^6 \times 15^{12}$

   15^{18}

4. $11^{12} \times 11^7$

   11^{19}

5. $(-w)^8 \times (-w)^{12}$

   $(-w)^{20}$

6. $(-12)^{18} \times (-12)^{13}$

   $(-12)^{31}$

7. $13^{10} \times 13^{15}$

   13^{25}

8. $w^{14} \times w^{12}$

   w^{26}

Divide. Write the quotient as one power.

9. $\dfrac{a^{25}}{a^{18}}$

   a^7

10. $\dfrac{(-13)^{14}}{(-13)^9}$

    $(-13)^5$

11. $\dfrac{14^{12}}{14^8}$

    14^4

12. $\dfrac{18^{11}}{18^5}$

    18^6

13. $\dfrac{19^{15}}{19^4}$

    19^{11}

14. $\dfrac{21^{22}}{21^{20}}$

    21^2

15. $\dfrac{(-x)^{17}}{(-x)^7}$

    $(-x)^{10}$

16. $\dfrac{25^8}{25^3}$

    25^5

Write the product or quotient as one power.

17. $r^9 \times r^8$

    r^{17}

18. $\dfrac{16^{20}}{16^{10}}$

    16^{10}

19. $\dfrac{x^{15}}{x^9}$

    x^6

20. $(-17)^8 \times (-17)^7$

    $(-17)^{15}$

21. $27^7 \times 27^6$

    27^{13}

22. $\dfrac{m^{16}}{m^{10}}$

    m^6

23. $(-b)^{21} \times (-b)^{14}$

    $(-b)^{35}$

24. $\dfrac{26^{17}}{26^5}$

    26^{12}

25. $(-s)^{11} \times (-s)^4$

    $(-s)^{15}$

26. Hampton has a baseball card collection of 5^6 cards. He organizes the cards into boxes that hold 5^4 each. How many boxes will Hampton need to hold the cards? Write the answer as one power.

    5^2

27. Write the expression for a number used as a factor seventeen times being multiplied by a number used as a factor fourteen times. Then write the product as one power.

    $x^{17} \times x^{14} = x^{31}$

Holt Middle School Math

Name _____ Date _____ Class _____

Homework and Practice
Looking for a Pattern in Integer Exponents

Evaluate the powers of 10.

1. 10^{-6} **2.** 10^4 **3.** 10^{-3} **4.** 10^5

_____0.000001_____   _____10,000_____   _____0.001_____   _____100,000_____

5. 10^{-1} **6.** 10^8 **7.** 10^{-5} **8.** 10^2

_____0.1_____   _____100,000,000_____   _____0.00001_____   _____100_____

Evaluate.

9. $(-7)^{-3}$

$-\dfrac{1}{343}$

10. $\dfrac{11^2}{11^5}$

$\dfrac{1}{1,331}$

11. $\dfrac{a^8}{a^{14}}$

$\dfrac{1}{a^6}$

12. $(-8)^{-4}$

$\dfrac{1}{4,096}$

13. $6^{-3} \cdot 6^{-2}$

$\dfrac{1}{7,776}$

14. $\dfrac{5^9}{5^{13}}$

$\dfrac{1}{625}$

15. $14^{-2} \cdot 14^5$

$2,744$

16. $\dfrac{19^7}{19^9}$

$\dfrac{1}{361}$

17. $\dfrac{(-15)}{(-15)^4}$

$-\dfrac{1}{3,375}$

18. $(-17)^{-3} \cdot (-17)^6$

$-4,913$

19. $\dfrac{21^2}{21^4}$

$\dfrac{1}{441}$

20. $(20)^3 \cdot (20)^{-5}$

$\dfrac{1}{400}$

Express the answer using powers of 10 and negative numbers.

21. 1 meter = $\dfrac{1}{1000}$ km = _____10^{-3}_____ km.

22. Find the volume of a cube with a side that measures 0.01 cm.
(Hint: $V = s^3$).

_____10^{-6} cm^3_____

Holt Middle School Math

LESSON 2-9 Homework and Practice
Scientific Notation

Write each number in standard notation.

1. 6.12×10^2 **2.** 7.9×10^{-3} **3.** 4.87×10^4 **4.** 9.3×10^{-2}

    612   0.0079   48,700   0.093

5. 8.06×10^3 **6.** 5.7×10^{-4} **7.** 3.17×10^{-5} **8.** 9.00613×10^{-2}

    8,060   0.00057   0.0000317   0.0900613

9. 9.85×10^{-5} **10.** 6.004×10^7 **11.** 8.23×10^4 **12.** 1.48×10^{-6}

    0.0000985   60,040,000   82,300   0.00000148

Write each number in scientific notation.

13. 108,000,000   **14.** 0.5943   **15.** 42   **16.** 0.0000673

    1.08×10^8 5.943×10^{-1} 4.2×10^1 6.73×10^{-5}

17. 0.0056   **18.** 6004   **19.** 0.00852   **20.** 24,631,500

    5.6×10^{-3} 6.004×10^3 8.52×10^{-3} 2.46315×10^7

21. 89450   **22.** 0.005702   **23.** 8,005,000,000   **24.** 0.00012805

    8.945×10^4 5.702×10^{-3} 8.005×10^9 1.2805×10^{-4}

25. The mass of the Earth is 5,980,000,000,000,000,000,000,000 kilograms. Write this number in scientific notation.

    5.98×10^{24}

26. The mass of a dust particle is 7.53×10^{-10}. Write this number in standard notation.

    0.000000000753 kg

Holt Middle School Math

Name _____ Date _____ Class _____

Homework and Practice
Rational Numbers

Simplify.

1. $\dfrac{6}{12}$

   $\dfrac{1}{2}$

2. $\dfrac{6}{24}$

   $\dfrac{1}{4}$

3. $\dfrac{12}{36}$

   $\dfrac{1}{3}$

4. $-\dfrac{8}{32}$

   $-\dfrac{1}{4}$

5. $\dfrac{15}{27}$

   $\dfrac{5}{9}$

6. $-\dfrac{16}{24}$

   $-\dfrac{2}{3}$

7. $-\dfrac{12}{96}$

   $-\dfrac{1}{8}$

8. $\dfrac{12}{54}$

   $\dfrac{2}{9}$

Write each decimal as a fraction in simplest form.

9. 0.56

   $\dfrac{14}{25}$

10. 3.2

    $3\dfrac{1}{5}$

11. 0.036

    $\dfrac{9}{250}$

12. −2.05

    $-2\dfrac{1}{20}$

13. 3.502

    $3\dfrac{251}{500}$

14. 0.064

    $\dfrac{8}{125}$

15. −8.4

    $-8\dfrac{2}{5}$

16. 0.004

    $\dfrac{1}{250}$

17. −0.70

    $-\dfrac{7}{10}$

18. 5.25

    $5\dfrac{1}{4}$

19. 0.128

    $\dfrac{16}{125}$

20. 0.0004

    $\dfrac{1}{2,500}$

Write each fraction as a decimal.

21. $\dfrac{3}{8}$

    0.375

22. $\dfrac{5}{9}$

    $0.55\bar{5}$

23. $\dfrac{21}{8}$

    2.625

24. $\dfrac{17}{18}$

    $0.94\bar{4}$

25. $\dfrac{19}{3}$

    $6.33\bar{3}$

26. $\dfrac{11}{20}$

    0.55

27. $\dfrac{7}{5}$

    1.4

28. $\dfrac{54}{36}$

    1.5

29. Make up a fraction that cannot be simplified that has 25 as its denominator.

    sample answer: $\dfrac{3}{25}$

Holt Middle School Math

Name _____ Date _____ Class _____

Homework and Practice

Adding and Subtracting Rational Numbers

1. Benjamin paid his cell phone bill that was $25.95. He wrote a check that cost $0.75 to pay the bill. When he mailed it, Benjamin put a $0.37 stamp on the letter. What was the total cost for Benjamin to pay his cell phone bill?

$27.07

2. Dannika is preparing a recipe that calls for $2\frac{3}{4}$ cups of flour. If Dannika has only $2\frac{1}{4}$ cups left in the flour container, how much flour must she add from a new bag to complete the recipe?

$\frac{1}{2}$ cup

Use a number line to find each sum.

3. $-0.3 + 0.8$

4. $-\frac{4}{5} + \frac{3}{5}$

0.5

$-\frac{1}{5}$

Add or subtract. Write answers in simplest form.

5. $\frac{5}{7} + \frac{1}{7}$

$\frac{6}{7}$

6. $-\frac{1}{8} - \frac{5}{8}$

$-\frac{3}{4}$

7. $\frac{5}{12} - \frac{1}{12}$

$\frac{1}{3}$

8. $\frac{3}{16} + \frac{5}{16}$

$\frac{1}{2}$

9. $\frac{2}{15} - \frac{8}{15}$

$-\frac{2}{5}$

10. $\frac{7}{20} - \frac{3}{20}$

$\frac{1}{5}$

11. $-\frac{5}{18} - \frac{7}{18}$

$-\frac{2}{3}$

12. $-\frac{3}{25} + \frac{11}{25}$

$\frac{8}{25}$

Evaluate each expression for the given value of the variable.

13. $92.7 + x$ for $x = 4.8$

97.5

14. $27.3 + x$ for $x = -9.5$

17.8

15. $\frac{5}{24} + x$ for $x = -\frac{7}{24}$

$-\frac{1}{12}$

Holt Middle School Math

Name _____ Date _____ Class _____

Homework and Practice
Multiplying Rational Numbers

Multiply. Write each answer in simplest form.

1. $6\left(\dfrac{2}{3}\right)$

$\underline{\quad 4 \quad}$

2. $-9\left(\dfrac{1}{3}\right)$

$\underline{\quad -3 \quad}$

3. $-8\left(-\dfrac{3}{16}\right)$

$\underline{\quad 1\frac{1}{2} \quad}$

4. $-14\left(\dfrac{3}{7}\right)$

$\underline{\quad -6 \quad}$

5. $\dfrac{5}{12}\left(-\dfrac{6}{25}\right)$

$\underline{\quad -\dfrac{1}{10} \quad}$

6. $-\dfrac{1}{12}\left(\dfrac{18}{5}\right)$

$\underline{\quad -\dfrac{3}{10} \quad}$

7. $\dfrac{1}{3}\left(\dfrac{18}{2}\right)$

$\underline{\quad 3 \quad}$

8. $-\dfrac{5}{12}\left(-\dfrac{6}{15}\right)$

$\underline{\quad \dfrac{1}{6} \quad}$

9. $-\dfrac{5}{6}\left(-\dfrac{12}{20}\right)$

$\underline{\quad \dfrac{1}{2} \quad}$

10. $\dfrac{7}{24}\left(-\dfrac{12}{35}\right)$

$\underline{\quad -\dfrac{1}{10} \quad}$

11. $\dfrac{19}{24}\left(-\dfrac{12}{57}\right)$

$\underline{\quad -\dfrac{1}{6} \quad}$

12. $\dfrac{18}{33}\left(-\dfrac{11}{54}\right)$

$\underline{\quad -\dfrac{1}{9} \quad}$

Multiply.

13. $3.1(2.6)$

$\underline{\quad 8.06 \quad}$

14. $-0.72(0.05)$

$\underline{\quad -0.036 \quad}$

15. $(8)(-5.8)$

$\underline{\quad -46.4 \quad}$

16. $-4(-5.56)$

$\underline{\quad 22.24 \quad}$

17. $-0.08(-6.02)$

$\underline{\quad 0.4816 \quad}$

18. $0.7(-9.3)$

$\underline{\quad -6.51 \quad}$

19. $(-1.14)(9.5)$

$\underline{\quad -10.83 \quad}$

20. $(-6.5)(-3.6)$

$\underline{\quad 23.4 \quad}$

21. $18(-0.15)$

$\underline{\quad -2.7 \quad}$

22. $(-4.32)(7.1)$

$\underline{\quad -30.672 \quad}$

23. $-11.3(-6.2)$

$\underline{\quad 70.06 \quad}$

24. $(8.516)(3.25)$

$\underline{\quad 27.677 \quad}$

Evaluate $3\dfrac{1}{4}x$ **for each value of x.**

25. $x = -3$

$\underline{\quad -9\frac{3}{4} \quad}$

26. $x = -\dfrac{2}{3}$

$\underline{\quad -2\frac{1}{6} \quad}$

27. $x = 2$

$\underline{\quad 6\frac{1}{2} \quad}$

28. $x = \dfrac{1}{2}$

$\underline{\quad 1\frac{5}{8} \quad}$

29. Blaine repaired a damaged car in $8\dfrac{1}{2}$ hours. He received $26.50 an hour for his work. How much was Blaine paid for repairing the car?

$\underline{\quad \$225.25 \quad}$

Holt Middle School Math

Name _____ Date _____ Class _____

Homework and Practice
Dividing Rational Numbers

Divide. Write each answer in simplest form.

1. $\dfrac{1}{4} \div \dfrac{5}{8}$

    $\dfrac{2}{5}$

2. $-\dfrac{5}{6} \div \dfrac{5}{12}$

    -2

3. $-\dfrac{2}{5} \div \dfrac{7}{10}$

    $-\dfrac{4}{7}$

4. $-\dfrac{3}{14} \div \left(-\dfrac{6}{7}\right)$

    $\dfrac{1}{4}$

5. $\dfrac{7}{9} \div \left(\dfrac{5}{6}\right)$

    $\dfrac{14}{15}$

6. $\dfrac{9}{20} \div \left(-\dfrac{3}{4}\right)$

    $-\dfrac{3}{5}$

7. $-\dfrac{11}{12} \div \left(-\dfrac{44}{54}\right)$

    $1\dfrac{1}{8}$

8. $-\dfrac{13}{30} \div \left(\dfrac{39}{45}\right)$

    $-\dfrac{1}{2}$

9. $20 \div \dfrac{4}{9}$

    45

10. $\dfrac{7}{8} \div (-21)$

    $-\dfrac{1}{24}$

11. $-10 \div \dfrac{4}{5}$

    $-12\dfrac{1}{2}$

12. $-\dfrac{21}{25} \div (-14)$

    $\dfrac{3}{50}$

Divide.

13. $32 \div 0.4$

    80

14. $-6.58 \div 0.08$

    -82.25

15. $7.26 \div (-0.03)$

    -242

16. $3.333 \div 0.66$

    5.05

17. $0.0096 \div (-1.2)$

    -0.008

18. $-25.28 \div 1.6$

    -15.8

19. $17.5 \div 0.07$

    250

20. $279.4 \div 12.7$

    22

21. $71.46 \div 9$

    7.94

22. $36.3 \div (-1.6)$

    -22.6875

23. $-984.6 \div 2.4$

    -410.25

24. $-601.96 \div 2.02$

    -298

Evaluate each expression for the given value of the variable.

25. $\dfrac{52}{x}$ for $x = -0.16$

    -325

26. $\dfrac{-14.52}{x}$ for $x = 5.5$

    -2.64

27. $\dfrac{-54.72}{x}$ for $x = -0.003$

    $18{,}240$

28. A 3.6-pound beef roast cost $10.62. What is the cost of the beef roast per pound?

    $2.95 per pound

Holt Middle School Math

Homework and Practice

LESSON 3-5 *Adding and Subtracting with Unlike Denominators*

Add or subtract. Write the answer in simplest form.

1. $\frac{1}{2} - \frac{3}{8}$
$\frac{1}{8}$

2. $\frac{3}{5} + \frac{1}{4}$
$\frac{17}{20}$

3. $\frac{7}{9} - \frac{5}{12}$
$\frac{13}{36}$

4. $-\frac{5}{9} + \frac{2}{3}$
$\frac{1}{9}$

5. $\frac{3}{10} - \left(-\frac{1}{2}\right)$
$\frac{4}{5}$

6. $\frac{7}{12} + \left(-\frac{5}{15}\right)$
$\frac{1}{4}$

7. $-\frac{4}{15} - \frac{2}{5}$
$-\frac{2}{3}$

8. $\frac{5}{12} - \frac{2}{5}$
$\frac{1}{60}$

9. $-\frac{7}{8} + \frac{5}{12}$
$-\frac{11}{24}$

10. $-2\frac{1}{8} - 3\frac{1}{4}$
$-5\frac{3}{8}$

11. $-4\frac{3}{5} + 1\frac{2}{3}$
$-2\frac{14}{15}$

12. $6\frac{1}{3} - 4\frac{5}{6}$
$1\frac{1}{2}$

13. $7 - 5\frac{7}{8}$
$1\frac{1}{8}$

14. $8\frac{1}{6} + \left(-\frac{7}{12}\right)$
$7\frac{7}{12}$

15. $-16 + \left(-\frac{8}{9}\right)$
$-16\frac{8}{9}$

16. $4\frac{7}{10} - 11$
$-6\frac{3}{10}$

Evaluate each expression for the given value of the variable.

17. $-2\frac{5}{8} + x$ for $x = 3\frac{1}{4}$
$\frac{5}{8}$

18. $1\frac{1}{2} + x$ for $x = -2\frac{5}{6}$
$-1\frac{1}{3}$

19. $-7\frac{4}{9} - x$ for $x = -7$
$-\frac{4}{9}$

20. $9\frac{5}{8} + x$ for $x = 6\frac{3}{4}$
$16\frac{3}{8}$

21. $-15\frac{3}{8} + x$ for $x = 1\frac{3}{4}$
$-13\frac{5}{8}$

22. $-15\frac{2}{9} - x$ for $x = -12\frac{2}{3}$
$-2\frac{5}{9}$

23. Brendan practiced soccer for $1\frac{1}{2}$ hours on Monday, $1\frac{1}{4}$ hours on Tuesday, $1\frac{1}{6}$ hours on Wednesday and $\frac{3}{4}$ hours on Thursday in preparation for the game on Friday. How many total hours did Brendan practice soccer in this week?

$4\frac{2}{3}$ hours

Holt Middle School Math

Name _____ Date _____ Class _____

Homework and Practice
Solving Equations with Rational Numbers

Solve.

1. $y - 3.2 = -4.7$

$\underline{\quad y = -1.5 \quad}$

2. $x + 5.61 = 3.89$

$\underline{\quad x = -1.72 \quad}$

3. $0.4d = 8.2$

$\underline{\quad d = 20.5 \quad}$

4. $b - 2 = 17.5$

$\underline{\quad b = 19.5 \quad}$

5. $a + 101 = -14.2$

$\underline{\quad a = -115.2 \quad}$

6. $3.3x = -108.9$

$\underline{\quad x = -33 \quad}$

7. $-19.48 + x = -28.03$

$\underline{\quad x = -8.55 \quad}$

8. $\dfrac{m}{10.1} = 3.5$

$\underline{\quad m = 35.35 \quad}$

9. $217.25 = 39.5w$

$\underline{\quad w = 5.5 \quad}$

10. $\dfrac{t}{4.7} = -14.7$

$\underline{\quad t = -69.09 \quad}$

11. $b - 29.15 = -17.73$

$\underline{\quad b = 11.42 \quad}$

12. $\dfrac{r}{-7.6} = 3.05$

$\underline{\quad r = -23.18 \quad}$

Solve. Write each in simplest form.

13. $\dfrac{5}{8} + y = 2\dfrac{3}{8}$

$\underline{\quad y = 1\dfrac{3}{4} \quad}$

14. $\dfrac{12}{25}m = -\dfrac{9}{50}$

$\underline{\quad m = -\dfrac{3}{8} \quad}$

15. $\dfrac{6}{35}r = \dfrac{18}{25}$

$\underline{\quad r = 4\dfrac{1}{5} \quad}$

16. $x - \left(-\dfrac{7}{10}\right) = 3\dfrac{3}{5}$

$\underline{\quad x = 2\dfrac{9}{10} \quad}$

17. $y - \dfrac{11}{18} = 4\dfrac{2}{9}$

$\underline{\quad y = 4\dfrac{5}{6} \quad}$

18. $-\dfrac{9}{24}w = \dfrac{18}{32}$

$\underline{\quad w = -1\dfrac{1}{2} \quad}$

19. Jessica baked 10 dozen cookies. She left $\dfrac{1}{8}$ of the baked cookies home and took the rest to school for the bake sale. How many cookies did Jessica take to school?

105 cookies

20. Doug must take 1.25 milliliters of medicine every day. How many days will the medicine last if Doug was given a prescription of the medicine in a bottle containing 50 milliliters?

40 days

Holt Middle School Math

Name _____ Date _____ Class _____

Homework and Practice

Solving Inequalities with Rational Numbers

Solve.

1. $-15.7 + y < 9.4$

$\underline{y < 25.1}$

2. $\dfrac{x}{-2.5} < -1.54$

$\underline{x > 3.85}$

3. $-6.2t \leq 14.57$

$\underline{t \geq -2.35}$

4. $\dfrac{x}{4.56} \geq -18.5$

$\underline{x \geq -84.36}$

5. $-16.87 + h \leq -15.92$

$\underline{h \leq 0.95}$

6. $-8.3w \geq -350.26$

$\underline{w \leq 42.2}$

Solve. Write answers in simplest form.

7. $w + \dfrac{9}{14} \geq \dfrac{5}{14}$

$\underline{w \geq -\dfrac{2}{7}}$

8. $x - \dfrac{11}{15} > \dfrac{4}{5}$

$\underline{x > 1\dfrac{8}{15}}$

9. $-\dfrac{10}{21}n \geq -2\dfrac{4}{7}$

$\underline{n \leq 5\dfrac{2}{5}}$

10. $4\dfrac{2}{3}y \leq -2\dfrac{4}{9}$

$\underline{y \leq -\dfrac{11}{21}}$

11. $\dfrac{x}{-14} < \dfrac{15}{28}$

$\underline{x > -7\dfrac{1}{2}}$

12. $a - 1\dfrac{7}{18} < -2\dfrac{5}{6}$

$\underline{a < -1\dfrac{4}{9}}$

13. $d - \left(-2\dfrac{8}{15}\right) > -3\dfrac{7}{10}$

$\underline{d > -6\dfrac{7}{30}}$

14. $x + \left(-3\dfrac{7}{12}\right) < -3\dfrac{5}{9}$

$\underline{x < \dfrac{1}{36}}$

15. $-4\dfrac{3}{8}y \leq -1\dfrac{3}{7}$

$\underline{y \geq \dfrac{16}{49}}$

16. Mr. Conner's students made kites in science class. He bought a 500-yd bolt of twine to tie to the kites. If he wants to give each student a piece of twine $33\dfrac{1}{3}$ yards long, what is the maximum number of pieces of twine Mr. Conner will be able to make from the bolt of twine?

$\underline{\text{15 pieces}}$

Holt Middle School Math

Homework and Practice

Squares and Square Roots

Find the two square roots for each number.

1. 16

2. 9

3. 64

4. 121

_4, −4_   _3, −3_   _8, −8_   _11, −11_

5. 36

6. 100

7. 225

8. 400

_6, −6_   _10, −10_   _15, −15_   _20, −20_

Evaluate each expression.

9. $\sqrt{27 + 37}$

10. $\sqrt{41 + 59}$

11. $\sqrt{122 - 41}$

12. $\sqrt{167 - 23}$

_8_   _10_   _9_   _12_

13. $3\sqrt{81} + 19$

14. $25 - \sqrt{25}$

15. $\sqrt{169} - \sqrt{36}$

16. $\sqrt{196} + 25$

_30_   _20_   _7_   _39_

17. $\dfrac{\sqrt{81}}{9}$

18. $-4.9\sqrt{64}$

19. $\dfrac{\sqrt{225}}{\sqrt{25}}$

20. $\dfrac{\sqrt{100}}{-2.5}$

_1_   _−39.2_   _3_   _−4_

21. Find the product of six and the sum of the square roots of 100 and 225.

_150_

22. Find the difference between the square root of 361 and the square root of 289.

_2_

23. If a replica of the ancient pyramids were built with a base area of 1,024 in.^{2}, what would be the length of each side?(Hint: $s = \sqrt{A}$)

_32 in._

24. The maximum displacement speed of a boat is found using the formula: Maximum Speed in km/h = 4.5 $\sqrt{}$the waterline length of the boat in meters. Find the maximum displacement speed of a boat that has a waterline length of 9 meters.

_13.5 km/h_

Holt Middle School Math

Name _____ Date _____ Class _____

Homework and Practice
Finding Square Roots

Each square root is between two integers. Name the integers.

1. $\sqrt{10}$ 2. $\sqrt{24}$ 3. $\sqrt{51}$ 4. $\sqrt{39}$

$3 < \sqrt{10} < 4$ $4 < \sqrt{24} < 5$ $7 < \sqrt{51} < 8$ $6 < \sqrt{39} < 7$

5. $\sqrt{66}$ 6. $\sqrt{30}$ 7. $\sqrt{78}$ 8. $\sqrt{87}$

$8 < \sqrt{66} < 9$ $5 < \sqrt{30} < 6$ $8 < \sqrt{78} < 9$ $9 < \sqrt{87} < 10$

Use a calculator to find each value. Round to the nearest tenth.

9. $\sqrt{18}$ 10. $\sqrt{63}$ 11. $\sqrt{19}$ 12. $\sqrt{41}$

4.2   7.9   4.4   6.4

13. $\sqrt{53}$ 14. $\sqrt{98}$ 15. $\sqrt{54}$ 16. $\sqrt{72}$

7.3   9.9   7.3   8.5

17. $\sqrt{83}$ 18. $\sqrt{120}$ 19. $\sqrt{200}$ 20. $\sqrt{489}$

9.1   11   14.1   22.1

21. The distance a person can see at sea is measured in miles by using the formula $d = \sqrt{\frac{3}{2}h}$, where h is the height in ft above sea level. About how many miles can a person see that is 8 feet above sea level? Round the answer to the nearest tenth of a mile.

3.5 miles

22. The length of the hypotenuse of a right triangle is the square root of the sum of the squares of the measures of the other two legs of the triangle. Approximate the length of the hypotenuse of a right triangle if the legs have measures 12 and 15.

19.2

23. At an accident scene, a police officer may determine the rate of speed, r, in mi/h, of the car by using the following formula $r = \sqrt{20\ell}$, where ℓ is length of the skid marks. How fast was a car going if the skid marks at the scene are 180 ft long?

60 mph

Holt Middle School Math

Homework and Practice

The Real Numbers

Write all names that apply to each number.

1. $\sqrt{\dfrac{36}{4}}$

integer, rational,

real, whole

2. $-\dfrac{3}{16}$

rational, real

3. $\sqrt{0.81}$

rational, real

4. -81

integer, rational, real

5. $-7.23\overline{3}$

rational, real

6. $\sqrt{95}$

irrational, real

State if the number is rational, irrational, or not a real number.

7. $\sqrt{49}$

rational

8. $-\sqrt{144}$

rational

9. $\dfrac{9}{\sqrt{3}}$

irrational

10. $\dfrac{\sqrt{81}}{\sqrt{9}}$

rational

11. $\dfrac{21}{0}$

not real

12. $\dfrac{20}{8}$

rational

13. $\sqrt{-100}$

not real

14. 8.67

rational

Find a real number between each pair of numbers.

15. $4\dfrac{2}{5}$ and $4\dfrac{3}{5}$

sample answer: $4\dfrac{1}{2}$

16. 7.25 and $\dfrac{15}{2}$

sample answer: 7.3

17. $\dfrac{5}{8}$ and $\dfrac{3}{4}$

sample answer: $\dfrac{7}{10}$

18. Give an example of a rational number between $-\sqrt{36}$ and $\sqrt{36}$

sample answer; 1

19. Give an example of an irrational number less than 0.

sample answer; $-\sqrt{3}$

20. Give an example of a number that is not real.

sample answer; $\sqrt{-54}$

Holt Middle School Math

Homework and Practice
LESSON 4-1 *Samples and Surveys*

Identify the population and sample. Give a reason why the sample could be biased.

1. The customers at a diner are surveyed to determine the number of times that local people eat out in a week.

   population *local people*

   sample *all the customers of the diner*

   possible bias *people already eating out are more likely to eat out*

2. At a school with school colors of purple and white, the male students are asked to name their favorite color.

   population *students at the school*

   sample *male students surveyed*

   possible bias *will say their school colors*

3. The first one thousand adults at a professional baseball game are surveyed and asked to name their favorite sport.

   population *all the people at the game*

   sample *adults surveyed*

   possible bias *already at a baseball game*

Identify the sampling method used.

4. The supervisor of the recreational committee visits 5 of the city's pools and collects water samples from the pools at various times of the day.

   stratified

5. Commuters on a subway are selected at random and asked to name their favorite flavor of ice cream.

   random

6. The register receipt of every 10th shopper at a grocery store is automatically compiled into a data base of the total amount spend and the items purchased.

   systematic

Holt Middle School Math

Name _____ Date _____ Class _____

Homework and Practice
Organizing Data

1. Use the given data to make a table.

Two hundred people were asked which was their favorite type of movie—comedy, drama, or action. The men's choices were 10 for comedy, 35 for drama and 55 for action. The women's choices were 45 for comedy, 50 for drama and 5 for action.

Choice	Comedy	Drama	Action
Men	10	35	55
Women	45	50	5

List the data values in the stem-and-leaf plot.

2.
```
1 | 2  5  7  8
2 | 0  0  6
3 | 1  1  2  2
4 | 5  6          key: 4 | 5 = 45
```

12, 15, 17, 18, 20, 20, 26,

31, 31, 32, 32, 45, 46

3.
```
4 | 4  6  8
5 | 0  2  4  6
6 | 7
8 | 1  3  5  7     key: 8 | 1 = 81
```

44, 46, 48, 50, 52, 54,

56, 67, 81, 83, 85, 87

4. Use the given data to make a stem-and-leaf plot.

Michael's Test Scores					
86	85	92	75	72	94
81	86	94	77	67	80

```
6 | 7
7 | 2  5  7
8 | 0  1  5  6  6
9 | 2  4  4
key: 9 | 2 = 92
```

5. Use the given data to make a back-to-back stem-and-leaf plot.

MLB American League—Central Division 2000–2001 Final Standings		
MLB Team	**Wins**	**Losses**
Cleveland	91	71
Minnesota	85	77
Chicago	83	79
Detroit	66	96
Kansas City	65	97

```
Wins   |   | Losses
6  5   | 6 |
       | 7 | 1  7  9
5  3   | 8 |
    1  | 9 | 6  7
```

key: | 9 | 6 represents 96

3 | 8 | represents 83

Holt Middle School Math

Name _____ Date _____ Class _____

Homework and Practice
LESSON 4-3 *Central Tendency*

Find the mean, median, and mode of each data set.

1. 9, 5, 8, 5, 9, 8, 4, 8, 7

mean: _____ 7 _____

median: _____ 8 _____

mode: _____ 8 _____

2. 8.3, 3.8, 4.2, 6.4, 3.9, 7.7, 4.2

mean: _____ 5.5 _____

median: _____ 4.2 _____

mode: _____ 4.2 _____

3. 41, 43, 44, 42, 44, 45, 42, 47, 43, 46

mean: _____ 43.7 _____

median: _____ 43.5 _____

mode: _____ 42, 43, 44 _____

4. 2, 27, 6, 47, 22, 6, 11, 8, 52, 6, 25, 19

mean: _____ 19.25 _____

median: _____ 15 _____

mode: _____ 6 _____

5. The Baylus family's food bills for the last 6 months were $362, $354, $412, $415, $354 and $353. What is the mean, median, and mode of the food bills for this time period?

mean: $375; median: $358; mode: $354

Use the data to find each answer.

Oceans		
	Area in sq. mi.	Greatest Known Depth in ft.
Pacific Ocean	64,000,000	36,198
Atlantic Ocean	31,815,000	30,246
Indian Ocean	25,300,000	24,460
Artic Ocean	5,440,200	18,456

6. Find the mean of the areas in square miles.

31,638,800 sq. mi.

7. Find the median of the area in square miles.

28,557,500 sq. mi.

8. Find the mean and median of the greatest known depth in feet.

mean: 27,340 ft; median: 27,353 ft

Holt Middle School Math

Name _____ Date _____ Class _____

Homework and Practice
Variability

Find the range and the first and third quartiles for each data set.

1. 52, 36, 41, 48, 55, 31, 57

range: _____26_____

first quartile: _____36_____

third quartile: _____55_____

2. 26, 28, 42, 43, 22, 56, 51, 36

range: _____34_____

first quartile: _____27_____

third quartile: _____47_____

Use the given data to make a box-and-whisker plot.

3. 44, 56, 30, 73, 34, 55, 62, 51

     10 20 30 40 50 60 70 80

4. 26, 37, 45, 62, 55, 11, 27, 72, 51, 48, 43, 38, 47

     10 20 30 40 50 60 70 80 90 100

Use the box-and-whisker plots to compare the data sets.

Data Set 2

Data Set 1

     10 20 30 40 50 60 70 80 90 100

5. Compare the ranges and medians.

The range of data set 2 is greater than the range of data set 1. The

median of data set 1 is greater than the median of data set 2.

6. Compare the ranges of the middle half of the data for each.

The range of the middle half of data set 1 is greater than the middle half

of data set 2.

Holt Middle School Math

Name _____ Date _____ Class _____

Homework and Practice

LESSON 4-5 *Displaying Data*

1. Organize the data into a frequency table and make a bar graph.

5 3 8 4 7 8 8 4 8 4 5 7 4 6 5 3 8 7 7 4 8

Number	Frequency
3	2
4	5
5	3
6	1
7	4
8	6

2. Use the data to make a histogram with intervals of 5.

Minutes it takes students to travel to school			
6	10	15	18
10	20	25	20
15	10	8	5
20	15	10	15
18	6	20	15

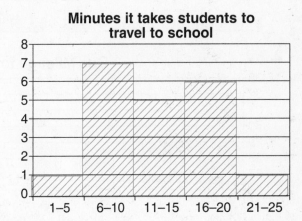

3. Make a line graph of the given data. Use the graph to estimate the percent of food expenses away from home in 1993.

Percent of Food Expenses Away from Home			
1960	19.9%	1980	32.2%
1965	22.8%	1985	35.8%
1970	26.3%	1990	36.7%
1975	28.5%	1995	38.2%

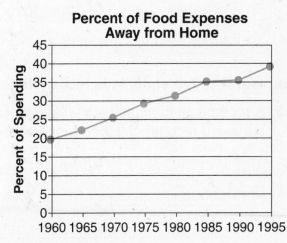

In 1993, approximately ____37____% of food expenses were away from the home.

Holt Middle School Math

Name _____ Date _____ Class _____

Homework and Practice
Misleading Graphs and Statistics

Explain why each graph is misleading.

1.

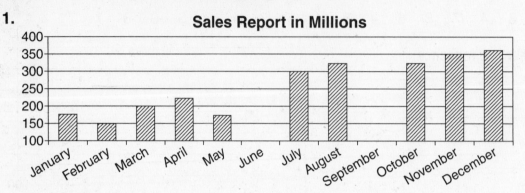

Sales Report in Millions

This graph is misleading because the vertical axis does not begin at zero.
Also, several of the month's sales figures are missing. This does not give
a true picture of increases and decreases or total sales for the year.

2.

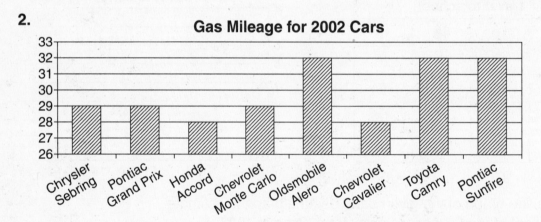

Gas Mileage for 2002 Cars

This graph is misleading because the vertical axis does not begin at zero.
This does not give a true comparison of the gas mileage for these vehicles.

Explain why the statistic is misleading.

3. A toothpaste company advertises that 9 out of 10 dentists
surveyed recommend their brand of toothpaste to their patients.

This statistic is misleading because the company does not say how many
dentists were surveyed to ask what brand of toothpaste they recommend.
Also, it is important if these dentists were paid for their responses or if
they received and distributed free samples to their patients.

Holt Middle School Math

Name _____ Date _____ Class _____

1. Use the given data to make a scatter plot.

Sandwich	Calories	Total Fat Grams
Chicken Breast	318	2
Chicken Teriyaki	374	1.5
Club	323	2
Cold Cut	441	7
Ham	288	1.5
Meatball	527	10
Roast Beef	293	2
Tuna	445	6
Turkey Breast	281	1.5
Veggie	226	1

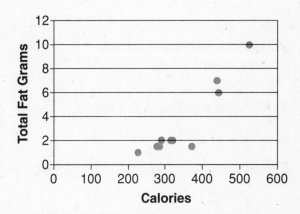

Do the data sets have a positive, a negative, or no correlation?

1. The type of car a person drives and the color of their hair.

no correlation

3. The number of people working on a job and the hours to completion.

negative correlation

4. The number of innings completed in a baseball game and the number of runs scored.

positive correlation

5. The number of shares of stock owned and the amount received in dividends.

positive correlation

6. Use the data to predict the percent of U.S. Households with a computer in 1998.

Percent of U.S. Households with a Computer				
Year	1985	1990	1995	2000
Percent	8.2%	15%	24.1%	51%

In 1998, about ____36____ % of U.S. households had a computer.

Holt Middle School Math

Name _____ Date _____ Class _____

1. Name four points in the figure. Possible answers are given.

_W, X, Y, Z_ _____

2. Name a line in the figure.

$\overleftrightarrow{WX}$ _____

3. Name the plane in the figure.

WXY _____

4. Name three segments in the figure.

$\overline{WX}$, $\overline{XY}$, or $\overline{WZ}$ _____

5. Name four rays in the figure.

$\overrightarrow{WX}$, $\overrightarrow{XW}$, $\overrightarrow{XY}$, or $\overrightarrow{WZ}$ _____

6. Name a right angle in the figure.

∠AXB _____

7. Name two acute angles in the figure

∠BXC and ∠CXD _____

8. Name two obtuse angles in the figure.

∠AXC and ∠CXE _____

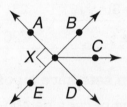

9. Name a pair of complementary angles in the figure.

∠BXC and ∠CXD _____

10. Name three pair of supplementary angles in the figure.

∠AXB and ∠BXD, ∠DXE and

∠AXE, ∠AXB and ∠EXD _____

In the figure, ∠1 and ∠2 are vertical angles.

11. If $m\angle 1 = 103°$, find $m\angle 2$.

$m\angle 2 = 103°$ _____

12. If $m\angle 2 = 115°$, find $m\angle 1$.

$m\angle 1 = 115°$ _____

Holt Middle School Math

Name _____ Date _____ Class _____

Homework and Practice
Parallel and Perpendicular Lines

1. Measure the angles formed by the transversal and the parallel lines. Which angles seem to be congruent.

   $\underline{\angle 1 \cong \angle 3 \cong \angle 5 \cong \angle 7 \text{ and}}$

   $\underline{\angle 2 \cong \angle 4 \cong \angle 6 \cong \angle 8}$

In the figure, line *x* ∥ line *y*. Find the measure of each indicated angle, if the *m* ∠ 8 = 34°.

2. ∠2	3. ∠3	4. ∠4
34°	146°	34°
5. ∠6	6. ∠7	7. ∠1
34°	146°	146°

In the figure, line *m* ∥ line *n*. Find the measure of each angle, if *m* ∠ 1 = 131°.

8. ∠2	9. ∠3	10. ∠4
49°	131°	49°
11. ∠5	12. ∠6	13. ∠7
131°	49°	131°

In the figure, line *a* ∥ line *b*.

14. Name all angles congruent to ∠5.

   $\underline{\angle 1, \angle 3, \angle 7}$

15. Name all angles congruent to ∠4.

   $\underline{\angle 2, \angle 6, \angle 8}$

16. Name three pairs of angles with sums of 180°.

   $\underline{\angle 1 + \angle 2, \angle 3 + \angle 4, \angle 5 + \angle 6, \angle 7 + \angle 8,}$

   $\underline{\angle 1 + \angle 8, \angle 2 + \angle 7, \angle 3 + \angle 6, \text{ or } \angle 4 + \angle 5}$

17. Which line is the transversal?

   $\underline{\text{line } m}$

Holt Middle School Math

Name _____ Date _____ Class _____

Homework and Practice
Triangles

1. Find *a* in the right triangle.

_____ **38°** _____

2. Find *b* in the acute triangle.

_____ **78°** _____

3. Find *m* in the acute triangle.

_____ **68°** _____

4. Find *y* in the right triangle.

_____ **43°** _____

5. Find *t* in the right triangle.

_____ **44°** _____

6. Find *x* in the obtuse triangle

_____ **38°** _____

7. Find *a* in the right triangle.

_____ **45°** _____

8. Find *x* in the right triangle.

_____ **42°** _____

Holt Middle School Math

Name _____ Date _____ Class _____

Homework and Practice
Polygons

Find the sum of the angle measures in each figure.

1.

180°

2.

360°

3.

720°

4.

360°

5.

540°

6.

360°

Find the angle measure in each regular polygon.

7.

90°

8.

60°

9.

120°

10.

144°

11.

135°

12.

108°

Write all the names that apply to each figure.

13.

quadrilateral

trapezoid

14.

quadrilateral

parallelogram

rectangle

15.

quadrilateral

parallelogram

rhombus

Holt Middle School Math

Homework and Practice

Coordinate Geometry

Determine if the slope of each line is positive, negative, 0, or undefined. Then find the slope of each line.

1. $\overleftrightarrow{AD}$

___negative; −1___

2. $\overleftrightarrow{BC}$

___positive; 1___

3. $\overleftrightarrow{MW}$

___0___

4. $\overleftrightarrow{TD}$

negative; $-\dfrac{2}{3}$

5. $\overleftrightarrow{SV}$

___positive; 1___

6. $\overleftrightarrow{RS}$

___undefined___

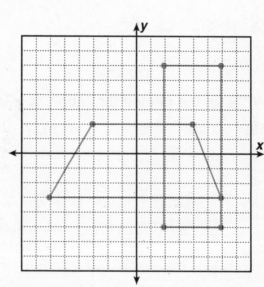

7. Which lines are parallel?

___$\overleftrightarrow{BC} \parallel \overleftrightarrow{SV}$___

8. Which lines are perpendicular?

___$\overleftrightarrow{MW} \perp \overleftrightarrow{RS}$; $\overleftrightarrow{AD} \perp \overleftrightarrow{BC}$; $\overleftrightarrow{TD} \perp \overleftrightarrow{XY}$___

___$\overleftrightarrow{AD} \perp \overleftrightarrow{SV}$___

Graph the quadrilaterals with the given vertices. Write all the names that apply to each quadrilateral.

9. (−3, 2), (−6, −4), (4, 2), (6, −4)

___quadrilateral, trapezoid___

10. (2, 6), (6, −5), (2, −5), (6, 6)

___quadrilateral, parallelogram, rectangle___

Holt Middle School Math

Name _____ Date _____ Class _____

Write a congruence statement for each pair of polygons.

1.

<u>triangle *ABW* ≅ triangle *CDX*</u> _____

2.

<u>rectangle *BDMR* ≅ rectangle *ACNS*</u> _____

3.

<u>pentagon *DMSXW* ≅ pentagon *BRNTZ*</u> _____

4.

<u>rhombus *DMTX* ≅ rhombus *KNSY*</u> _____

Find the value of the variable if triangle *ABC* is congruent to triangle *XYZ*.

5. Find *a*.

___41°___

6. Find *b*.

___108°___

7. Find *c*.

___31°___

8. Find *x*.

___18___

9. Find *y*.

___21___

10. Find *z*.

___14___

41

Holt Middle School Math

Name _____ Date _____ Class _____

LESSON 5-7 Homework and Practice
Transformations

Identify each as a translation, rotation, reflection, or none of these.

1.

<u>translation or reflection</u>

2.

<u>rotation</u>

3.

<u>rotation</u>

4.

<u>reflection</u>

Draw the image of the triangle after each transformation.

5. reflection across $\overline{BC}$

6. translation along $\overline{AB}$ so that C' coincides with B.

Draw the image of the rectangle with vertices $(-1, 6)$, $(-3, 4)$, $(3, 6)$, $(5, 4)$ after each transformation.

7. translation 5 units down

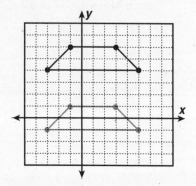

8. 270° clockwise rotation around $(0, 0)$

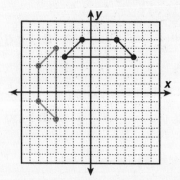

Holt Middle School Math

Homework and Practice

Symmetry

Complete the figure. The dashed line is the line of symmetry.

1.

2.

3.

4.

5.

6.

Complete the figure. The point is the center of rotation.

7.

8.

9.

10.

Holt Middle School Math

LESSON 5-9 Homework and Practice
Tessellations

1. Name a possible combination of squares and triangles that would form a semiregular tessellation.

3 triangles, 2 squares

2. Create a semiregular tessellation that uses squares and triangles.

sample answer: _____

3. Create another semiregular tessellation that uses squares and triangles.

sample answer: _____

4. Create a tessellation with quadrilateral *ABCD*.

sample answer: _____

5. Use rotations to create a variation of the tessellation in Exercise 4.

sample answer: _____

Holt Middle School Math

Name _____ Date _____ Class _____

Homework and Practice

LESSON 6-1 *Perimeter and Area of Rectangles and Parallelograms*

Find the perimeter of each figure.

1.

	33	
19		19
	33	

104 units

2.

24
17 / 17
24

82 units

3.

	16.25	
19.5		19.5
	16.25	

71.5 units

Graph each figure with the given vertices. Then find the area of each figure.

4. (−4, 3), (−7, −3), (4, −3), (7, 3)   **5.** (−7, 7), (−7, −7), (7, −7), (7, 7)

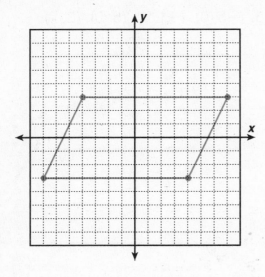

66 units²   **196 units²**

6. Mrs. Delfina is having new carpet installed in a room and hall in her home. The diagram at the right shows the dimensions of the area. If the carpet costs $1.95 a square foot, how much will it cost Mrs. Delfina to carpet the area?

18 ft
12.5 ft   3 ft
16 ft

$532.35

Name _____ Date _____ Class _____

Homework and Practice

Perimeter and Area of Triangles and Trapezoids

Find the perimeter of each figure.

1.

21.7
11.6
15.8
9.2

58.3 units

2.

$5\frac{1}{2}$
$3\frac{1}{8}$
$4\frac{1}{4}$

$12\frac{7}{8}$ units

3.

$3\frac{3}{4}$
$2\frac{5}{8}$
$2\frac{5}{8}$
$1\frac{11}{12}$

$10\frac{11}{12}$ units

Graph and find the area of each figure with the given vertices.

4. $(-6, -7), (2, -7), (-3, 4)$

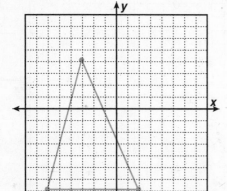

44 units^2

5. $(-5, 0), (-1, 4), (5, 0), (2, 4)$

26 units^2

6. $(-1, 7), (4, 7), (-3, -4), (6, -4)$

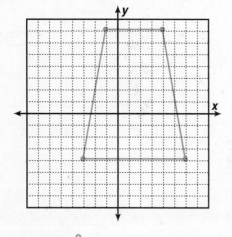

77 units^2

7. $(-6, 2), (6, 2), (6, -4)$

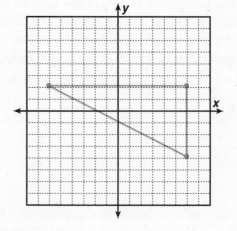

36 units^2

Holt Middle School Math

Name _____ Date _____ Class _____

Homework and Practice
The Pythagorean Theorem

Find the length of the hypotenuse in each triangle.

1.
9
12

<u>15</u>

2.
24
10

<u>26</u>

3.
36
27

<u>45</u>

4. Graph the triangle formed with coordinates
(−7, 0), (−7, −6), (1, 0) and find the length
of the hypotenuse.

<u>10</u>

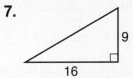

**Solve for the unknown side in each right
triangle. Round the answers to the nearest
hundredth.**

5.
48
14

<u>50</u>

6.
3.6
2.7

<u>4.5</u>

7.
9
16

<u>18.36</u>

8.
15
22

<u>26.63</u>

9.
28
21

<u>35</u>

10.
26
24

<u>35.38</u>

11.
9
20

<u>21.93</u>

12.
36
32

<u>48.17</u>

13.
34
12

<u>36.06</u>

14. Use the Pythagorean Theorem to find the height of the triangle
at the right. Then use the height to find the area of the triangle.

65
60

<u>$h = 25$; area = 750 units^2</u>

Holt Middle School Math

CHAPTER 6-4 Homework and Practice
Circles

Find the circumference of each circle, both in terms of π and to the nearest tenth of a unit. Use 3.14 for π.

1. circle with diameter 12 cm

   <u>12π cm or 37.7 cm</u>

2. circle with radius 11 in.

   <u>22π in. or 69.1 in.</u>

3. circle with radius 17 ft

   <u>34π ft or 106.8 ft</u>

4. circle with diameter 28 yd

   <u>28π yd or 87.9 yd</u>

5. circle with radius 10.8 in.

   <u>21.6π in. or 67.8 in.</u>

6. circle with diameter 23.6 m

   <u>23.6π m or 74.1 m</u>

Find the area of each circle, both in terms of π and to the nearest tenth of a unit. Use 3.14 for π.

7. circle with diameter 12 yd

   <u>36π yd^2 or 113.0 yd^2</u>

8. circle with radius 16 cm

   <u>256π cm^2 or 803.8 cm^2</u>

9. circle with radius 30 ft

   <u>900π ft^2 or 2,826 ft^2</u>

10. circle with diameter 38 m

   <u>361π m^2 or 1,133.5 m^2</u>

11. circle with radius 8.9 m

   <u>79.2π m^2 or 248.7 m^2</u>

12. circle with diameter 56 m

   <u>784π m^2 or 2,461.8 m^2</u>

13. Graph a circle with center (0, 0) that passes through (0, −5). Find the area and circumference, both in terms of π and to the nearest tenth of a unit. Use 3.14 for π.

   <u>$A = 25\pi$ units^2 or 78.5 units^2;</u>

   <u>$C = 10\pi$ units or 31.4 units</u>

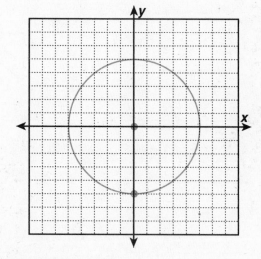

14. If a circle has an area of 7,850 yd^2, what is the diameter of the circle? Use 3.14 for π.

   <u>50 yd</u>

Holt Middle School Math

Homework and Practice

6-5 Drawing Three-Dimensional Figures

1. Use isometric dot paper to sketch a rectangular box that is 4 units long, 2 units wide, and 3 units tall.

2. Use isometric dot paper to sketch a cube that is 3 units on each edge.

3. Sketch a one-point perspective drawing of a triangular prism.

sample answer:

4. Sketch a two-point perspective drawing of a rectangular box.

sample answer:

Holt Middle School Math

Name _____ Date _____ Class _____

Homework and Practice
Volume of Prisms and Cylinders

Find the volume to the nearest tenth of a unit. Use 3.14 for π.

1.

<u>512 ft³</u>

2.

<u>1,177.5 cm³</u>

3.

<u>1,120 yd³</u>

4.

<u>56,160 mm³</u>

5.

<u>2,208 in.³</u>

6.

<u>4,220.2 cm³</u>

7.

<u>3,048.6 in.³</u>

8.

<u>480 m³</u>

9.

<u>1,056 cm³</u>

10. A cylinder has a radius of 8 cm and a height of 20 cm. Explain whether tripling the height will triple the volume of the cylinder.

The original cylinder has a volume of 1,280π cm³. If you triple the height the volume is 3,840π cm³, which is triple the original volume.

11. Find the height of a cylinder if the volume is 2,512 in.³ and the radius is 10 in. Use 3.14 for π.

<u>8 in.</u>

12. What is the volume of a can of peanuts with a height of 5 in. and a lid that is 4 in. wide? Use 3.14 for π. Round the answer to the nearest tenth of an inch.

<u>62.8 in.³</u>

Holt Middle School Math

LESSON 6-7

Homework and Practice
Volume of Pyramids and Cones

Find the volume of each figure to the nearest tenth of a unit. Use 3.14 for π.

1.

8 in.

6 in.

_____75.4 in.³_____

2.

4 m

6 m   6 m

_____48 m³_____

3.

3 ft

2 ft

_____12.6 ft³_____

4.

24 m

10 m   9.5 m

_____760 m³_____

5.

15 cm

16 cm

_____942 cm³_____

6.

36 cm

25 cm   25 cm

_____7,500 cm³_____

7. A funnel has a diameter of 8 in. and is 21 in. deep. What is the volume of the funnel to the nearest tenth of a unit? Use 3.14 for π

351.7 in.³

8. The radius of a cone is 13 ft and its height is 27 ft. Find the volume of the cone to the nearest tenth. Use 3.14 for π.

4,775.9 ft³

9. Find the volume of a rectangular pyramid if the height is 35 cm and the base sides are 21 cm and 28 cm.

6,860 cm³

10. The base of a regular pyramid has an area of 135 in.². The height of the pyramid is 8.5 in. Find the volume.

382.5 in.³

Holt Middle School Math

LESSON 6-8 Homework and Practice
Surface Area of Prisms and Cylinders

Find the surface area of each figure to the nearest of a tenth unit. Use 3.14 for π.

1.

   ___1,752 ft²___

2.

   ___4,615.8² in.___

3.

   ___2,820 yd²___

4.

   ___8,664 cm²___

5.

   ___251.2 m²___

6.

   ___308 m²___

7.

   ___480 cm²___

8.

   ___2,524.6 ft²___

9.

   ___2007.6 in²___

10. Find the surface area to the nearest tenth of a unit of a cylinder 84.5 m tall that has a diameter of 50 m. Use 3.14 for π.

    ___17,191.5 m²___

11. Find the surface area to the nearest tenth of a unit of a rectangular prism with height 24 cm and sides 18 cm and 14 cm.

    ___2,040 cm²___

12. A recipe calls for a 9 × 13 × 2 in. baking dish to have the inside of the baking dish coated before adding the recipe contents. What is the surface area of the baking dish that will be coated?

    ___205 in.²___

Holt Middle School Math

Name _____ Date _____ Class _____

LESSON 6-9 Homework and Practice
Surface Area of Pyramids and Cones

Find the surface area of each figure to the nearest of a tenth
unit. Use 3.14 for π.

1.

20 cm → 40 cm

$\underline{3{,}768 \text{ cm}^2}$

2.

28 in.

19 in.

19 in.

$\underline{1{,}425 \text{ in.}^2}$

3.

17 ft → 30 ft

$\underline{2{,}508.9 \text{ ft}^2}$

4.

4.5 m

3 m   3 m

$\underline{36 \text{ m}^2}$

5.

29.5 yd

14 yd

$\underline{1{,}912.3 \text{ yd}^2}$

6.

21.5 ft

12.5 ft

12.5 ft

$\underline{693.8 \text{ ft}^2}$

7.

30 in.

35 in.

$\underline{2{,}355 \text{ in.}^2}$

8.

32 cm

23 cm   23 cm

$\underline{2001 \text{ cm}^2}$

9.

26 m

19.6 m

19.6 m

$\underline{1{,}403.4 \text{ m}^2}$

10. Find the length of the slant height of a square pyramid if the one
side of the base is 26 cm and the surface area is 2,236 cm².

30 cm

11. Find the surface area of a regular square pyramid with a slant
height of 27 in. and a base perimeter of 96 in.

1,872 in.²

12. Find the length of the slant height of a cone with a radius of 40 ft
and a surface area of 9,420 ft². Use 3.14 for π.

35 ft

Holt Middle School Math

Name _____ Date _____ Class _____

Find the volume of each sphere, both in terms of π and to the nearest tenth of a unit. Use 3.14 for π.

1. $r = 12$ yd

$$\underline{2{,}304\pi \text{ yd}^3 \approx}$$
$$\underline{7{,}234.6 \text{ yd}^3}$$

2. $r = 27$ ft

$$\underline{26{,}244\pi \text{ ft}^3 \approx}$$
$$\underline{82{,}406.2 \text{ ft}^3}$$

3. $d = 36$ m

$$\underline{7{,}776\pi \text{ m}^3 \approx}$$
$$\underline{24{,}416.6 \text{ m}^3}$$

4. $d = 48$ ft

$$\underline{18{,}432\pi \text{ ft}^3 \approx}$$
$$\underline{57{,}876.5 \text{ ft}^3}$$

5. $r = 4.5$ m

$$\underline{121.5\pi \text{ m}^3 \approx}$$
$$\underline{381.5 \text{ m}^3}$$

6. $r = 7.5$ cm

$$\underline{562.5\pi \text{ cm}^3 \approx}$$
$$\underline{1{,}766.3 \text{ cm}^3}$$

7. $r = 33$ cm

$$\underline{47{,}916\pi \text{ cm}^3 \approx}$$
$$\underline{150{,}456.2 \text{ cm}^3}$$

8. $d = 32.02$ ft

$$\underline{5{,}471.6\pi \text{ ft}^3 \approx}$$
$$\underline{17{,}180.8 \text{ ft}^3}$$

9. $d = 60$ m

$$\underline{36{,}000\pi \text{ m}^3 \approx}$$
$$\underline{113{,}040 \text{ m}^3}$$

Find the surface area of each sphere, in terms of π and to the nearest tenth of a unit.

10. 5.6 in.

$$\underline{125.4\pi \text{ in.}^2 \approx}$$
$$\underline{393.8 \text{ in.}^2}$$

11. 12.4 yd

$$\underline{153.8\pi \text{ yd}^2 \approx}$$
$$\underline{482.9 \text{ yd}^2}$$

12. 25 cm

$$\underline{2{,}500\pi \text{ cm}^2 \approx}$$
$$\underline{7{,}850 \text{ cm}^2}$$

13. 36 ft

$$\underline{1{,}296\pi \text{ ft}^2 \approx}$$
$$\underline{4{,}069.4 \text{ ft}^2}$$

14. 14.1 cm

$$\underline{198.8\pi \text{ cm}^2 \approx}$$
$$\underline{624.3 \text{ cm}^2}$$

15. 21.5 in.

$$\underline{1{,}849\pi \text{ in.}^2 \approx}$$
$$\underline{5{,}805.9 \text{ in.}^2}$$

16. Estimate to the nearest tenth of an inch the surface area of a baseball with a 3 in. diameter. Use 3.14 for π.

$$\underline{28.3 \text{ in.}^2}$$

Holt Middle School Math

Homework and Practice

LESSON 7-1

7-1 Ratios and Proportions

Find two ratios that are equivalent to each given ratio.

1. $\frac{7}{35}$

sample $\frac{1}{5}$, $\frac{14}{70}$

2. $\frac{4}{16}$

sample $\frac{1}{4}$, $\frac{8}{32}$

3. $\frac{16}{48}$

sample $\frac{1}{3}$, $\frac{10}{30}$

4. $\frac{7}{8}$

sample $\frac{14}{16}$, $\frac{21}{24}$

5. $\frac{24}{6}$

sample $\frac{8}{2}$, $\frac{48}{12}$

6. $\frac{1}{2}$

sample $\frac{3}{6}$, $\frac{5}{10}$

7. $\frac{14}{30}$

sample $\frac{7}{15}$, $\frac{21}{45}$

8. $\frac{16}{6}$

sample $\frac{32}{12}$, $\frac{8}{3}$

9. $\frac{25}{45}$

sample $\frac{5}{9}$, $\frac{10}{18}$

Simplify to tell whether the ratios form a proportion.

10. $\frac{10}{60}$ and $\frac{2}{12}$

yes, $\frac{1}{6} = \frac{1}{6}$

11. $\frac{10}{24}$ and $\frac{30}{72}$

yes, $\frac{5}{12} = \frac{5}{12}$

12. $\frac{8}{27}$ and $\frac{16}{56}$

no, $\frac{8}{27} \neq \frac{2}{7}$

13. $\frac{9}{36}$ and $\frac{13}{40}$

no, $\frac{1}{4} \neq \frac{13}{40}$

14. $\frac{14}{27}$ and $\frac{42}{81}$

yes, $\frac{14}{27} = \frac{14}{27}$

15. $\frac{15}{25}$ and $\frac{20}{30}$

no, $\frac{3}{5} \neq \frac{2}{3}$

16. $\frac{16}{28}$ and $\frac{20}{35}$

yes, $\frac{4}{7} = \frac{4}{7}$

17. $\frac{17}{68}$ and $\frac{14}{56}$

yes, $\frac{1}{4} = \frac{1}{4}$

18. Mr. Blackwell had two ties for every five shirts he owned. If he owned 25 shirts, how many ties did he own?

10 ties

19. The school had the classroom walls painted. Seven out of 10 people surveyed liked the new color of the walls. Of the 250 people surveyed, how many people liked the new color of the walls?

175

Holt Middle School Math

LESSON 7-2 Homework and Practice
Ratios, Rates and Unit Rates

For exercises 1–3, use the bar graph to find each rate.

1. Helena's salary per week

   $650 _____

2. Aisha's salary per day

   $145 _____

3. Nani's salary per hour

   $22.50 _____

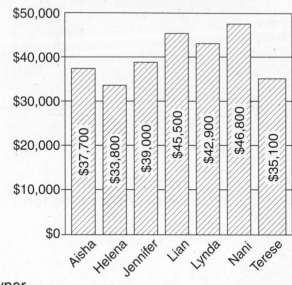

**Yearly Gross Salary
Based on 52 Weeks,
5 Days a Week, 8 Hours a Day**

4. Of the 405 students who took the test, 162 of them passed. Write a ratio in simplest form for the number of students who passed the test to the number of students who took the test.

   $\dfrac{2}{5}$

5. A lawn care company charges a homeowner $1,625 a year to maintain a lawn that is 65 ft by 50 ft. What is the maintenance fee per square foot?

   $0.50 per square foot _____

6. A 12 oz container of soda has 180 calories, how many calories are in one ounce of the soda?

   15 calories _____

Determine the better buy.

7. a 500-count ream of paper for $8.25 or a 1250-count ream of paper for $20

   1250-count ream for $20 _____

8. a 1.5 lb bag of carrots for $2.85 or a 2 lb bag of carrots for $3.84

   1.5 lb bag for $2.85 _____

9. Morgan paid $16.74 for 12.4 gallons of gasoline. What was the cost per gallon?

   $1.35 per gallon _____

Holt Middle School Math

Name _____ Date _____ Class _____

Homework and Practice
Problem Solving Skill: Analyze Units

Find the appropriate factor for each conversion.

1. millimeters to meters

$$\frac{1 \text{ m}}{1000 \text{ mm}}$$

2. inches to yards

$$\frac{1 \text{ yd}}{36 \text{ in.}}$$

3. days to minutes

$$\frac{1440 \text{ min}}{1 \text{ day}}$$

4. Oliver constructs a fence around a garden that is 24 feet by 36 feet. How many yards of fencing does Oliver need?

40 yards

5. Marci drinks four 48 ounce glasses of water a day. How many pints of water does she drink every day?

12 pints

6. Christopher wrestles for his high school in the light heavyweight division. Christopher weighs 175 pounds. How many ounces does he weigh?

2800 ounces

7. Mari bought $9\frac{1}{2}$ yards of ribbon. How many inches of ribbon did she buy?

342 inches

8. A bag of frozen vegetables weighs 64 ounces. How many pounds does the package of vegetables weigh?

4 pounds

9. The 18th hole on the local golf course is 543 yards long. How many feet is the distance of this par 5 hole?

1,629 feet

A Boeing 777-300 commercial jetliner has a maximum take-off weight of 660,000 pounds, wing span of 199 feet 11 inches, overall length of 242 feet 4 inches, and an interior cabin width of 19 feet 3 inches. Find the following dimensions of the plane.

10. What is the maximum take-off weight in tons? **330 tons**

11. What is the measure of the wing span in inches? **2,399 inches**

12. What is the overall length of the plane in yards? **80.77 yards**

Holt Middle School Math

LESSON 7-4 Homework and Practice
Solving Proportions

Tell whether each pair of ratios are proportional.

1. $\frac{5}{6} \overset{?}{=} \frac{30}{36}$ 2. $\frac{8}{20} \overset{?}{=} \frac{6}{14}$ 3. $\frac{12}{27} \overset{?}{=} \frac{8}{18}$ 4. $\frac{13}{15} \overset{?}{=} \frac{39}{45}$

    yes   no   yes   yes

5. $\frac{8}{16} \overset{?}{=} \frac{50}{100}$ 6. $\frac{21}{49} \overset{?}{=} \frac{14}{36}$ 7. $\frac{18}{24} \overset{?}{=} \frac{9}{15}$ 8. $\frac{4}{18} \overset{?}{=} \frac{18}{81}$

    yes   no   no   yes

9. $\frac{16}{10} \overset{?}{=} \frac{26}{20}$ 10. $\frac{24}{14} \overset{?}{=} \frac{36}{21}$ 11. $\frac{25}{16} \overset{?}{=} \frac{5}{4}$ 12. $\frac{17}{11} \overset{?}{=} \frac{51}{33}$

    no   yes   no   yes

Solve each proportion.

13. $\frac{4}{15} = \frac{a}{45}$ 14. $\frac{16}{18} = \frac{8}{w}$ 15. $\frac{m}{11} = \frac{32}{44}$ 16. $\frac{12}{t} = \frac{4}{7}$

    $a = 12$ $w = 9$ $m = 8$ $t = 21$

17. $\frac{9}{b} = \frac{27}{72}$ 18. $\frac{x}{36} = \frac{21}{27}$ 19. $\frac{6}{y} = \frac{18}{51}$ 20. $\frac{10}{32} = \frac{15}{x}$

    $b = 24$ $x = 28$ $y = 17$ $x = 48$

21. $\frac{45}{81} = \frac{n}{27}$ 22. $\frac{28}{21} = \frac{44}{t}$ 23. $\frac{d}{42} = \frac{49}{147}$ 24. $\frac{17}{r} = \frac{102}{78}$

    $n = 15$ $t = 33$ $d = 14$ $r = 13$

25. The Orlemann family planted 3 rows of corn this year and harvested 270 ears. How many rows should they plant if they want to harvest 360 ears of corn?

    4 rows

26. Find the number of times a heart beats in 2 minutes if it beats 576 times in 8 minutes.

    144 times

27. David is making chocolate-chip cookies. Chocolate chips cost $1.79 for 12 ounces. David buys 60 ounces of chocolate chips for the cookies. How much did the chocolate chips cost?

    $8.95

Holt Middle School Math

Homework and Practice

LESSON 7-5 *Dilations*

Tell whether each transformation is a dilation.

1.

_____ dilation _____

2.

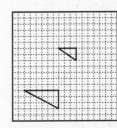

_____ not a dilation _____

Dilate each figure by the given scale factor with *P* as the center of dilation.

3. scale factor is 2

4. scale factor is $\frac{1}{3}$

Dilate each figure by the given scale with the origin as the center of dilation. What are the coordinates of the image?

5. scale factor is 2

_____ (1,8), (8,0), (8,8) _____

6. scale factor is $\frac{1}{3}$

_____ (0,0), (4,0), (2,−2), (0,−2) _____

7. scale factor is 3

___ (−6,6), (6,6), (6,−6), (−6,−6) ___

8. scale factor is $\frac{1}{4}$

___ (−3,3), (−2,3), (−2,1), (−3,1) ___

Holt Middle School Math

Name _____ Date _____ Class _____

1. Which figures are similar to *ABCD*?

all figures are similar

2. If a tree casts a 22-ft shadow at the same time a 6-ft tall person casts a 4-ft shadow, how tall is the tree?

33 ft

3. In △*RST*, *RS* = 28 cm, *ST* = 20 cm, *RT* = 24 cm. If △*DKM* is similar to △*RST* and the ratio of the corresponding sides of △*DKM* to △*RST* is 3 to 4, find the lengths of $\overline{DK}$, $\overline{KM}$, and $\overline{DM}$.

DK = 21 cm, KM = 15 cm, DM = 18 cm

4. A nickel is approximately 20 mm in diameter and a quarter is approximately 25 mm in diameter. If the nickel is enlarged to a diameter of 128 mm, what would be the diameter of the quarter using the same scale?

160 mm

5. The students gave their school a gift of an American flag that measures 30 ft by 50 ft. They wanted to make a scale drawing of the flag to place on a plaque acknowledging the gift. What would the dimensions of the flag on the plaque be if it were made to a scale of 10 ft = 1 in.?

3 in. × 5 in.

6. Lilly is enlarging a photo that is 4 in. wide and 6 in. long to a photo that is 24 in. wide. What would be the length of the new photo after the enlargement?

36 in.

7. A 4 ft tall child is standing by The Leaning Tower of Pisa in Italy. The child casts a 15 ft shadow at the same time the tower casts a 675 ft shadow. Approximate the height of the Leaning Tower of Pisa.

180 ft

Holt Middle School Math

Homework and Practice
LESSON 7-7 *Scale Drawings*

The scale of a drawing is $\frac{1}{4}$ in. = 12 ft. Find the actual measurement.

1. 8 in.

___384 ft___

2. 11 in.

___528 ft___

3. 16 in.

___768 ft___

4. 18 in.

___864 ft___

5. 22 in.

___1,056 ft___

6. 27 in.

___1,296 ft___

7. 21.5 in.

___1,032 ft___

8. 38.5 in.

___1,848 ft___

The scale is 2 cm = 15 m. Find the length each measurement would be on a scale drawing.

9. 180 m

___24 cm___

10. 585 m

___78 cm___

11. 330 m

___44 cm___

12. 420 m

___56 cm___

13. 225 m

___30 cm___

14. 622.5 m

___83 cm___

15. 547.5 m

___73 cm___

16. 682.5 m

___91 cm___

17. On a map the distance between Charleston and Mt. Pleasant is 3.2 cm. The scale is 1 cm = 25 mi. What is the actual distance in miles between these two towns?

___80 mi___

18. Blueprints of a building are drawn with a scale of 1 cm = 25 ft. If the base of the building is a square with a perimeter 700 feet, what is the length of one side of the base of the building on the scale drawing?

___7 cm___

19. If the scale drawing of a room has measurements of 8 cm by 4.5 cm and the scale of the drawing is 1 cm = 8 ft, what are the actual measurements of the room?

___64 ft × 36 ft___

Holt Middle School Math

LESSON 7-8

Homework and Practice

Scale Models

Tell whether each scale reduces, enlarges, or preserves the size of the actual object.

1. 1 in.:15 in.

_____reduces_____

2. 3 ft:1 yd.

_____preserves_____

3. 1 cm:1 in.

_____reduces_____

4. 40 cm:10 in.

_____enlarges_____

5. 1,760 yd:1 mi

_____preserves_____

6. 1 mi:1 km

_____enlarges_____

Change both measurements to the same unit of measure, and find the scale factor.

7. 2-in. model of a 5-ft desk

_____1:30_____

8. 4-ft model of a 120-yd field

_____1:90_____

9. 30-cm model of a 7.5-m wall

_____1:25_____

10. 50-in. model of a 7,000-ft volcano

_____1:1,680_____

11. The museum has a 2-ft model of a 10-yard shark. What is the scale factor of the model?

1:15

12. Marina made a scale model of her yard. Her yard is 40 ft × 28 ft 9 in. Her drawing is 16 in. × 11.5 in. What scale factor did she use?

1:30

13. A 17 in. model of a 2002 Buick Rendezvous is made with a scale factor of $\frac{1}{11}$. Estimate the actual length of a 2002 Buick Rendezvous?

187 in.

14. A miniature fireplace for a dollhouse is 4.5 in. by 6.75 in. If the scale factor is $\frac{1}{12}$, what size fireplace does the miniature represent?

54 in. × 81 in.

Holt Middle School Math

Name _____ Date _____ Class _____

Homework and Practice
Scaling 3-Dimensional Figures

A 15-in. cube is built from small cubes, each 1 in. on a side.
Compare the following values.

1. the side lengths of the two cubes

The sides of the 15-in. cube are 15 times as long as the sides of the

1-in. cube.

2. the surface area of the two cubes

The surface area of the 15-in. cube is 1,350 or 15^2 times that of the 1-in.

cube.

3. the volumes of the two cubes

The volume of the 15-in. cube is 3,375 or 15^3 times that of the 1-in. cube.

A 20-in. cube is built from small cubes, each 1 in. on a side.
Compare the following values.

4. the side lengths of the two cubes

The sides of the 20-in. cube are 20 times as long as the sides of the

1-in. cube.

5. the surface area of the two cubes

The surface area of the 20-in. cube is 2,400, or 20^2 times that of the

1-in. cube.

6. the volumes of the two cubes

The volume of the 20-in. cube is 8,000, or 20^3 times that of the 1-in. cube.

7. The dimensions of a warehouse are 180 ft long, 225 ft wide, and
90 ft high. The scale model used to build the warehouse is 15 in.
long. Find the width and height of the model of the warehouse.

18.75 in. wide and 7.5 in. high

8. A 4-cm × 3-cm × 5-cm solid figure is built with centimeter
cubes. If each dimension is doubled, how many cubes are used
to build the larger solid?

480 cubes

Holt Middle School Math

LESSON 8-1 Homework and Practice
Relating Decimals, Fractions, and Percents

Find the missing ratio or percent equivalent for each letter on the number line.

0%   100%
c   n   k   w   a   d   s   b
4% $\frac{1}{8}$ $\frac{1}{5}$ 35% $\frac{12}{25}$ 65%   78% $\frac{9}{10}$

1. *a*

48%

2. *b*

90%

3. *c*

$\frac{1}{25}$

4. *d*

$\frac{13}{20}$

5. *k*

20%

6. *n*

12.5%

7. *s*

$\frac{39}{50}$

8. *w*

$\frac{7}{20}$

Find each equivalent value.

9. 44% as a fraction

$\frac{11}{25}$

10. $\frac{3}{50}$ as a decimal

0.06

11. $\frac{13}{40}$ as a percent

32.5%

12. $\frac{3}{5}$ as a percent

60%

13. $11\frac{1}{9}$% as a fraction

$\frac{1}{9}$

14. $\frac{3}{8}$ as a decimal

0.375

15. At Eduardo's party, 18 friends attended but 6 friends could not come. What percent of the people invited could come to the party?

75%

16. On a math quiz, Ande answered 34 out of 40 questions correctly. What percent did she answer correctly?

85%

17. There are 300 students and 25 tables in the school cafeteria. If the students are seated equally at the tables, what percent of the students are seated at one table?

4%

Holt Middle School Math

Homework and Practice

Finding Percents

Find each percent.

1. What percent of 60 is 45?

   75%

2. 45 is what percent of 90?

   50%

3. What percent of 45 is 18?

   40%

4. What percent of 75 is 15?

   20%

5. 21 is what percent of 84?

   25%

6. 51 is what percent of 85?

   60%

7. What percent of 60 is 27?

   45%

8. What percent of 90 is 27?

   30%

9. 18 is what percent of 60?

   30%

10. 24.2 is what percent of 110?

    22%

11. What percent of 42 is 35?

    $83\frac{1}{3}\%$

12. What percent of 64 is 24?

    37.5%

13. What percent of 78 is 27.3?

    35%

14. 105 is what percent of 60?

    175%

15. An airplane completed 900 miles of a 1200-mile flight.
    What percent of the trip remains to be completed?

    25%

16. Cloe had 36 of the 45 questions on the math test correct.
    What percent of problems did Cloe have correct?

    80%

17. Lincoln received $55 for his birthday. He puts $22 of it in his
    savings account. What percent of the money did Lincoln deposit
    in his savings account?

    40%

18. Chico bought a jacket for $42. The cost of the jacket including tax,
    was $44.31. What was the percent of sales tax on the purchase?

    5.5%

Holt Middle School Math

Homework and Practice

LESSON
8-3 *Finding a Number When the Percent Is Known*

Find each number.

1. 25% of what number is 12?

_____48_____

2. 27 is 54% of what number?

_____50_____

3. 51 is 60% of what number?

_____85_____

4. 32% of what number is 8?

_____25_____

5. 80% of what number is 16?

_____20_____

6. 76 is 95% of what number?

_____80_____

7. 27 is 18% of what number?

_____150_____

8. 24% of what number is 72?

_____300_____

9. 104 is 65% of what number?

_____160_____

10. 12 is 3% of what number?

_____400_____

11. 5% of what number is 12.2?

_____244_____

12. 16% of what number is 4.8?

_____30_____

13. 90 is $66\frac{2}{3}$% of what number?

_____135_____

14. 40.5 is 150% of what number?

_____27_____

15. Meredith bought a bicycle that cost $385.89. In addition, she had to pay 7% sales tax on her purchase. What was the amount of sales tax Meredith paid? Round the answer to the nearest cent.

$27.01

16. Wilson answered 92% of a 25 question test correctly. How many questions did he answer correctly?

23

17. Rodriquez had $84.60 of his salary withheld for taxes. This was 15% of his gross pay. What is his gross pay?

$564

18. A car dealer receives an order of 340 new cars. Thirty percent of the cars are silver in color. How many of the cars received by the dealership are silver?

102

Holt Middle School Math

Name _____ Date _____ Class _____

Homework and Practice
Percent Increase and Decrease

Find each percent increase or decrease to the nearest percent.

1. from 16 to 12

___decrease 25%___

2. from 40 to 46

___increase 15%___

3. from 20 to 26

___increase 30%___

4. from 50 to 38

___decrease 24%___

5. from 75 to 45

___decrease 40%___

6. from 30 to 45

___increase 50%___

7. from 27 to 35.1

___increase 30%___

8. from 35 to 22.75

___decrease 35%___

9. from 84 to 54.6

___decrease 35%___

10. from 35 to 42.7

___increase 22%___

11. from 39 to 97.5

___increase 150%___

12. from 108 to 86.4

___decrease 20%___

13. from 63 to 39

___decrease 38%___

14. from 81 to 124

___increase 53%___

15. from 72 to 98

___increase 36%___

16. The regular price of track shoes is $49.75. They are on sale for $39.80. What is the percent of decrease for the sale price?

___20%___

17. An electronics store pays a $255.50 for a TV and sells it for $357.70. What is the percent of increase in the price of the TV?

___40%___

18. The Globe Company has laid off 1,220 employees of the company's 24,400 employees. What is the percent of decrease in the company's work force?

___5%___

19. Brooke is given a 4% raise which makes her salary $754 a week. What was Brooke's salary before the salary increase?

___$725___

20. Clyde weighed 200 pounds and lost 15 pounds. What was the percent of decrease in his weight?

___7.5%___

Holt Middle School Math

Homework and Practice

LESSON 8-5 *Estimating with Percents*

Estimate.

1. 26 out of 51

_____about 50%_____

2. 24% of 42

_____about 10_____

3. 19% of 20

_____about 4_____

4. 30% of 73

_____about 25_____

5. 68% of 103

_____about 70_____

6. 61 out of 82

_____about 75%_____

7. 32 out of 98

_____about 33%_____

8. 34 out of 84

_____about 40%_____

9. 50% of 19.6

_____about 10_____

Estimate each number or percent.

10. 10% of 81.2 is about what number?

_____about 8_____

11. 18 is 26% of about what number?

_____about 70_____

12. About what number is 33% of 46?

_____about 15_____

13. 32 is 39% of about what number?

_____about 80_____

14. On Tuesday, 453 students attend school. This is about 91% of the total enrollment. Estimate the school's total enrollment.

_____about 500 students_____

15. Suzette bought dinner for her friends. The total cost of the meals was $73.95. Suzette left a tip of $15. Approximate the percent of the tip to the cost of the meals.

_____about 20%_____

16. Of the 294 students who took the state test, 31 of them must retake the test. Estimate the percent of students who need to retake the test.

_____about 10%_____

17. The usual markup on shoes at Fast Times Department Store is 240%. During a 25%-off sale, the store sold a pair of shoes for $39.95. Estimate the amount of the store's profit on the shoes.

_____about $20_____

Holt Middle School Math

Homework and Practice

LESSON
8-6 *Applications of Percents*

Complete the table to find the amount of sales tax for each sale amount to the nearest cent.

1.

	6% sales tax	7% sales tax	5.5% sales tax
$53.50	$3.21	$3.75	$2.94
$80.50	$4.83	$5.64	$4.43
$219.95	$13.20	$15.40	$12.10
$2,640.00	$158.40	$184.80	$145.20

Complete the table to find the commission for each sale amount to the nearest cent.

2.

	5% commission	8% commission	7.5% commission
$365.00	$18.25	$29.20	$27.38
$2,140.00	$107.00	$171.20	$160.50
$16,300.00	$815.00	$1304.00	$1222.50
$94,750.00	$4,737.50	$7,580.00	$7,106.25

3. Mr. Darney bought a house for $58,000. He made a down payment of 20% and got a loan for the rest. What was the amount of his loan?

$46,400

4. Elijah buys three pens for $1.89 each and a notebook for $3.95. The sales tax rate is 6%. What is Elijah's total cost? Round the answer to the nearest cent.

$10.20

5. Seth is a real estate agent. He receives 8% commission on the selling price of any home he sells. If the last house he sold had a selling price of $145,900, what was Seth's commission?

$11,672

Holt Middle School Math

Name _____ Date _____ Class _____

Homework and Practice
Simple Interest

Find the missing value.

1. principal = $175
   rate = 4%
   time = 5 years
   interest = ?

   _____$35_____

2. principal = ?
   rate = 6%
   time = 6 years
   interest = $81

   _____$225_____

3. principal = $210
   rate = 5%
   time = ? years
   interest = $31.50

   _____3 years_____

4. principal = $125
   rate = ?%
   time = 4 years
   interest = $35

   _____7%_____

5. principal = ?
   rate = $5\frac{1}{4}$%
   time = 2 years
   interest = $126

   _____$1,200_____

6. principal = ?
   rate = 6.5%
   time = 3 years
   interest = $165.75

   _____$850_____

7. Scott deposits $1,000 in an account that earns 5% simple interest. What will the account be worth after two years?

   $1,100
   _____

8. A bank pays 5.5% simple interest per year. Find the total amount at the end of one year on a principal of $3,000.

   $3,165
   _____

9. Mr. Womer borrowed $1,100 to start his own business. National Bank charged him 15% interest per year. Mr. Womer paid $330 in interest. For what period of time did he borrow the money?

   2 years
   _____

10. Ms. Lang borrows $2,300 for 30 months at 13% interest per year. How much interest will Ms. Lang pay? What is the total amount she will repay?

    interest = $747.50; total amount repaid = $3,047.50
    _____

Holt Middle School Math

Homework and Practice
LESSON 9-1 *Probability*

The following table indicates the inventory totals for a shoe store. Find the probability for choosing the following types of shoes.

	Two-Tone	Black	White
High-Top	25	54	21
Low Cut	15	24	11

1. P(two-tone high-top)

$$\frac{1}{6}$$

2. P(black low cut)

$$\frac{4}{25}$$

3. P(white high top)

$$\frac{7}{50}$$

4. P(black shoe)

$$\frac{13}{25}$$

5. P(two-tone)

$$\frac{4}{15}$$

6. P(two-tone low cut)

$$\frac{1}{10}$$

7. P(blue shoe)

$$0$$

8. P(black or white)

$$\frac{11}{15}$$

9. P(low cut or high top)

$$1$$

Find the probability of drawing the following colored candies from a jar containing 25 red, 15 blue, 20 green, 30 yellow, and 10 orange pieces of candy.

10. P(yellow)

$$\frac{3}{10}$$

11. P(red)

$$\frac{1}{4}$$

12. P(orange)

$$\frac{1}{10}$$

13. P(blue)

$$\frac{3}{20}$$

14. P(purple)

$$0$$

15. P(blue or green)

$$\frac{7}{20}$$

16. P(candy)

$$1$$

17. P(red or yellow)

$$\frac{11}{20}$$

18. There are 25 red, 16 green, 30 purple, 14 white, 20 black, and 15 orange marbles in a bag. What is the probability of picking a marble that is not purple?

$$\frac{3}{4}$$

19. What is the probability of tossing a 4 on a regular numerical cube?

$$\frac{1}{6}$$

Holt Middle School Math

LESSON 9-2 # Homework and Practice
Experimental Probability

1. A number cube was thrown 125 times. The results are shown in the table below. Complete the table with the experimental probability for each outcome.

Outcome	1	2	3	4	5	6
Frequency	15	25	20	26	18	21
Probability	12%	20%	16%	20.8%	14.4%	16.8%

The school spirit wear shop sells special sweatshirts with the school logo imprinted on them in sizes small, medium, large, x-large and xx-large. In the first hour the store is open, the first 50 customers buy 2 small, 4 medium, 5 large, 15 x-large, and the rest buy xx-large. Find the probability of the purchase of each of the different size sweatshirts from the store.

2. P(x-large sweatshirt)

$\frac{3}{10}$ or 30%

3. P(medium sweatshirt)

$\frac{2}{25}$ or 8%

4. P(xx-large sweatshirt)

$\frac{12}{25}$ or 48%

5. P(small or large sweatshirt)

$\frac{7}{50}$ or 14%

If the store has 225 customers in the second hour they are open, predict how many sweatshirts of each size will be sold based on the purchases during the first hour.

6. number of small sweatshirts sold

9

7. number of medium sweatshirts sold

18

8. number of xx-large sweatshirts sold

108

9. number of large and x-large sweatshirts sold

90

10. Jay practiced his foul shots for the upcoming basketball game. He attempted 45 shots and made 36 of them. What is the probability that Jay would make the foul shot?

80%

11. If Jay took 20 foul shots in the basketball game, predict how many shots he would make based on his practicing.

16%

Holt Middle School Math

LESSON 9-3 Homework and Practice

Problem Solving Strategy: Use a Simulation

Use the table of random numbers for the problems below.

2596	3623	1053	2161	8550	9672	1044	9852	8935	8727
2393	1231	2795	2036	5138	7488	5814	2086	5397	8073
5086	9057	2050	7424	1706	1391	3585	3124	4164	9498
3274	5099	1789	7021	5636	2404	7180	3395	4734	0395
1387	7460	9196	0463	1388	5104	6408	7463	3289	9321
5891	8081	6222	9656	5606	8739	8698	3982	4974	9961
1544	2817	5296	1340	9750	3943	5697	1585	1097	8365
0442	3881	9080	7964	9357	8202	9987	5681	1288	7894
7170	4188	7099	7590	2158	0242	5299	4095	6986	3935
6039	5890	3996	0217	4045	6545	3744	8368	2034	8670

Ms. Patrick gave the same math test to all three of her math classes. In the first two classes, 70% of the students received a grade above C. Estimate the probability that at least 13 of 20 students will receive a grade above C in the third class.

1. Using the first row as the first trial, count the successful outcomes and name the unsuccessful outcomes.

13 out of 20 successful; 96, 85, 96, 72, 98, 89, 87

2. Using the second row, count the successful outcomes and name the unsuccessful outcomes.

12 out of 20 successful; 93, 95, 74, 88, 86, 97, 80, 73

Determine the successful outcomes in the remaining rows of the random number table.

3. third row   **4.** fourth row   **5.** fifth row   **6.** sixth row

13   13   12   10

7. seventh row   **8.** eighth row   **9.** ninth row   **10.** tenth row

14   8   12   16

11. Based on the simulation, estimate the probability that at least 13 of 20 students will receive a grade above C.

50%

Holt Middle School Math

Homework and Practice
Theoretical Probability

An experiment consists of rolling two fair dice. Find each probability.

1. P(total shown = 4)

$$\frac{1}{12}$$

2. P(total shown = 6)

$$\frac{5}{36}$$

3. P(total shown = 10)

$$\frac{1}{12}$$

4. P(total shown = 11)

$$\frac{1}{18}$$

5. P(total shown = 1)

$$0$$

6. P(total shown = 5)

$$\frac{1}{9}$$

7. P(total shown ≥ 2)

$$1$$

8. P(total shown ≤ 7)

$$\frac{7}{12}$$

9. P(total shown > 8)

$$\frac{5}{18}$$

Find the theoretical probability of having a thrown dart land in the indicated area.

10. P(landing in area A)

$$\frac{1}{2}$$

11. P(landing in area B)

$$\frac{1}{4}$$

12. P(landing in area C)

$$\frac{1}{8}$$

13. P(landing in area D)

$$\frac{1}{8}$$

14. P(landing in areas A or C)

$$\frac{5}{8}$$

15. What is the theoretical probability of winning a raffle if 375 tickets were sold and you bought 25?

$$\frac{1}{15}$$

16. The second place winner of the raffle could choose between 12 envelopes each with money in them. Two of the envelopes contained a $20 bill, 4 contained $10 bills, and 6 contained $5 bills. What is the theoretical probability that the winner will choose an envelope with a $20 bill in it?

$$\frac{1}{6}$$

Holt Middle School Math

Name _____ Date _____ Class _____

LESSON 9-5 **Homework and Practice**
The Fundamental Counting Principle

School identification codes at Truman School contain 1 letter followed by 3 numbers. All codes are equally likely.

1. Find the number of possible identification codes.

   26,000

2. Find the probability that an ID code of the school does not contain the number 0.

   $\dfrac{18954}{26000} = \dfrac{729}{1000} = 0.729$

3. The Dairy King Shop serves 3 flavors of ice cream: vanilla, chocolate, and vanilla/chocolate swirl. The ice cream can be served in a dish, sugar cone, or waffle cone and may be a small, medium, large, or jumbo size. Make a tree diagram indicating the possible outcomes for each ice cream served.

4. How many different ice cream selections does the Dairy King Shop have?

   36

Find the probability for each of the following. Assume all selections are equally likely.

5. P(dish of ice cream)

   $\dfrac{1}{3} = 0.33\overline{3}$

6. P(vanilla and small ice cream)

   $\dfrac{1}{12} = 0.08\overline{3}$

7. P(medium size)

   $\dfrac{1}{4} = 0.25$

8. P(not a dish)

   $\dfrac{2}{3} = 0.66\overline{6}$

Holt Middle School Math

Homework and Practice
Permutations and Combinations

Evaluate each expression.

1. 12!

$\underline{479,001,600}$

2. 9!

$\underline{362,880}$

3. 13! − 10!

$\underline{6,223,392,000}$

4. 11! − 8!

$\underline{39,876,480}$

5. $\frac{22!}{19!}$

$\underline{9,240}$

6. $\frac{20!}{15!}$

$\underline{1,860,480}$

7. $\frac{18!}{(24 - 12)!}$

$\underline{13,366,080}$

8. $\frac{21!}{(21 - 5)!}$

$\underline{2,441,880}$

9. $\frac{17!}{(23 - 14)!}$

$\underline{980,179,200}$

10. How many different 3 people committees can be formed from a group of 25 people?

$\underline{2,300}$

11. From a class of 28 students, how many different ways can 4 students be selected to serve on the student council as president, vice president, secretary and treasurer?

$\underline{491,400}$

12. The boys' volleyball team has 24 players. If the coach chooses 9 boys to play at a time, how many different teams can be formed?

$\underline{1,307,504}$

13. The golf tournament has 120 players signed up to play. How many different 4-person sets can be formed?

$\underline{8,214,570}$

14. Mr. Cruz bought new tires for his car. The dealer advised Mr. Cruz to have the tires rotated every 5,000 miles. If Mr. Cruz takes the advice of the dealer and has the tires rotated a different way every 5,000 miles, how many possible miles would he drive before using all the possible rotations?

$\underline{120,000 \text{ miles}}$

Holt Middle School Math

Homework and Practice
LESSON 9-7 *Independent and Dependent Events*

Determine if the events are dependent or independent.

1. spinning a spinner and rolling a numerical cube

   _____independent_____

2. drawing a card from a deck and not replacing it and then drawing another card

   _____dependent_____

3. selecting a piece of cake and selecting a drink

   _____independent_____

A jar contains 4 white chips, 5 purple chips, and 1 black chip. Chips are selected randomly one at a time, and are not replaced. Find the probability of the following.

4. P(purple then black)

$$\frac{1}{18} = 0.05\bar{5}$$

5. P(black then white)

$$\frac{2}{45} \approx 0.04\bar{4}$$

6. P(white then purple)

$$\frac{2}{9} = 0.2\bar{2}$$

7. P(purple then white)

$$\frac{2}{9} = 0.2\bar{2}$$

8. P(2 whites)

$$\frac{2}{15} = 0.13\bar{3}$$

9. P(2 purples)

$$\frac{2}{9} = 0.2\bar{2}$$

10. P(2 black chips)

$$0$$

11. P(white, then purple, then black)

$$\frac{1}{36} = 0.027\bar{7}$$

12. P(3 whites)

$$\frac{1}{30} = 0.03\bar{3}$$

13. Mrs. Benedict offers extra credit when she gives a math test. She writes the first 5 prime numbers on 5 separate cards and places them in a box. Students are permitted to draw one card to determine their extra credit when the test is finished. The cards are replaced after each student draws. What is the most extra credit a student can receive on a test? What is the probability of drawing that card?

11 extra credit points; probability is $\frac{1}{5}$

Holt Middle School Math

Homework and Practice

LESSON 9-8 *Odds*

1. If the probability of Courtney winning the raffle is $\frac{7}{12}$, what are the odds in favor of Courtney winning the raffle?

    <u>7 : 5</u>

2. The odds in favor of the New York Yankees winning the World Series are 5 to 3. What is the probability that the Yankees will win the World Series?

    $\frac{5}{8} = 0.625$

A bag contains 18 red jelly beans, 12 green jelly beans, 10 purple jelly beans, 6 yellow jelly beans, and 4 orange jelly beans.

3. Find P(green jelly bean)

    $\frac{6}{25} = 0.24$

4. Find P(red jelly bean)

    $\frac{9}{25} = 0.36$

5. Find P(yellow jelly bean)

    $\frac{3}{25} = 0.12$

6. Find the odds in favor of choosing a red jelly bean.

    <u>9 : 16</u>

7. Find the odds against choosing a red jelly bean.

    <u>16 : 9</u>

8. Find the odds in favor of choosing an orange jelly bean.

    <u>2 : 23</u>

9. Find the odds against choosing a purple jelly bean.

    <u>4 : 1</u>

10. Find the odds in favor of choosing a green jelly bean.

    <u>6 : 19</u>

11. Find the odds against choosing a yellow jelly bean.

    <u>22 : 3</u>

12. Find the odds in favor of not choosing an orange jelly bean.

    <u>23 : 2</u>

Holt Middle School Math

Homework and Practice

LESSON 10-1 *Solving Two-Step Equations*

Write and solve a two-step equation to answer the following questions.

1. Sue wants to buy a new printer that costs $189. She has $125 saved. She has a job that pays $8 an hour. How many hours must she work to earn enough to buy the printer?

x = number of hours

$189 = 8x + 125$

$189 - 125 = 8x + 125 - 125$

$64 = 8x$

$\dfrac{64}{8} = \dfrac{8x}{8}$

$8 = x$

2. Corbin's car payment is $289. This is $37 less than $\frac{1}{3}$ of his monthly income. What is Corbin's monthly income?

x = monthly income

$289 = \dfrac{1}{3}x - 37$

$289 + 37 = \dfrac{1}{3}x - 37 + 37$

$326 = \dfrac{1}{3}x$

$326 \times 3 = \left(\dfrac{1}{3}x\right) \times 3$

$978 = x$

Solve.

3. $13 = 3a - 14$
$a = 9$

4. $\dfrac{1}{3}k - 4 = 1$
$k = 15$

5. $-8 = \dfrac{x}{3} - 5$
$x = -9$

6. $6 - 5d = 1$
$d = 1$

7. $15y + 9 = -36$
$y = -3$

8. $\dfrac{1}{4}x + 6 = 11$
$x = 20$

9. $\dfrac{w}{4} - 9 = -3$
$w = 24$

10. $0.3m - 5 = 7$
$m = 40$

11. $\dfrac{x - 5}{7} = -3$
$x = -16$

12. $7 - \dfrac{a}{4.2} = 3.5$
$a = 14.7$

13. $\dfrac{5r - 3}{2} = -4$
$r = -1$

14. $-12.9 = 5.7 + 3d$
$d = -6.2$

15. Nineteen more than five times a number is eighty-four. Find the number.

13

16. Mr. Cruz buys some wood and pays $245. Each bundle of wood costs $15 and there is a delivery charge of $35. How many bundles of wood did Mr. Cruz buy?

14 bundles

Holt Middle School Math

LESSON 10-2 Homework and Practice
Solving Multistep Equations

Solve.

1. $8y - 4 - 7y = 11$

$\underline{\qquad y = 15 \qquad}$

2. $2x + 2 + 5x = 23$

$\underline{\qquad x = 3 \qquad}$

3. $8 = 7a - 8 - 3a$

$\underline{\qquad a = 4 \qquad}$

4. $r + 5r + 5 = -25$

$\underline{\qquad r = -5 \qquad}$

5. $9w - 12w - 2 = 7$

$\underline{\qquad w = -3 \qquad}$

6. $38 = 24 - 7x + 5x$

$\underline{\qquad x = -7 \qquad}$

7. $\frac{2}{7}y - \frac{5}{6} + \frac{5}{7}y = 1\frac{1}{6}$

$\underline{\qquad y = 2 \qquad}$

8. $\frac{5}{8}x + 1 - \frac{7}{8}x = \frac{3}{4}$

$\underline{\qquad x = 1 \qquad}$

9. $6x + 16 - 15x = -11$

$\underline{\qquad x = 3 \qquad}$

10. $\frac{4}{9}w + 6 - \frac{1}{3}w = 4$

$\underline{\qquad w = -18 \qquad}$

11. $0.05d - 0.2d - 17 = 13$

$\underline{\qquad d = -200 \qquad}$

12. $0.6m - 4.4 - 4.8m = 2.4$

$\underline{\qquad m \approx -1.62 \qquad}$

13. $8.2s + 4 - 13.7s = -7$

$\underline{\qquad s = 2 \qquad}$

14. $11y - 7.5 - 6y = 2$

$\underline{\qquad y = 1.9 \qquad}$

15. $13x - 4.6x - 3.9 = 8.7$

$\underline{\qquad x = 1.5 \qquad}$

16. The measure of an angle is 34° less than its supplement. Find the measure of each angle.

$\underline{\text{angle} = 73°; \text{ supplement} = 107°}$

17. The measure of an angle is 9° more than twice its complement. Find the measure of each angle.

$\underline{\text{angle} = 63°; \text{ complement} = 27°}$

18. If the perimeter of the triangle is 139. Find the measure of each side.

$\underline{RS = 24;\ ST = 48;\ RT = 67}$

Holt Middle School Math

Name _____ Date _____ Class _____

Homework and Practice

Solving Equations with Variables on Both Sides

Solve.

1. $5x - 1 = 21 + 3x$

$x = 11$

2. $9y + 3 = 6y - 15$

$y = -6$

3. $7w - 3 = w - 12.6$

$w = -1.6$

4. $12 + 8a = 3a - 3$

$a = -3$

5. $\frac{2}{9}n - 5 = 2 + \frac{5}{9}n$

$n = -21$

6. $1.8d + 31 = 3.4d + 19$

$d = 7.5$

7. $2b + 30 = 4b + 3$

$b = 13.5$

8. $4x + 2.3 = 2x - 3.7$

$x = -3$

9. $3(m - 5) = m - 7$

$m = 4$

10. $5(3h - 2) = 2(h + 8)$

$h = 2$

11. $5 + \frac{1}{2}y = \frac{3}{8}y + 6$

$y = 8$

12. $2\left(x - \frac{1}{2}\right) = 4\left(x + \frac{1}{4}\right)$

$x = -1$

13. $4(3r - 2) = 4 - 12r$

$r = \frac{1}{2}$

14. $\frac{1}{4}x - 7 = \frac{1}{3}x + 8$

$x = -180$

15. $\frac{3a - 4}{2} = 5 - 2a$

$a = 2$

16. Mandy and Mackenzie spent the same amount of money at the arcade. They both played the same number of games. Mandy played $0.50 games and spent $10 on refreshments. Mackenzie played $0.75 games and spent $6 on refreshments. How many games did each person play?

16 _____

17. The square and the equilateral triangle at the right have the same perimeter. Find the lengths of the sides of the square.

21 _____

Name _____ Date _____ Class _____

Solve and graph.

1. $5x + 3 \geq 28$

$$x \geq 5$$

2. $10 - \frac{1}{2}w > 12$

$$w < -4$$

3. $7y - 15 - 4y \leq -18$

$$y \leq -1$$

4. $7a < 12a + 10$

$$a > -2$$

5. $19 - 4m > 4m + 11$

$$m < 1$$

6. $-\frac{5}{6}d + 8 > 13$

$$d < -6$$

7. $2(3x + 1) \leq 4(2x - 3)$

$$x \geq 7$$

8. $14.1 - \frac{2}{5}h \geq 13.9 - \frac{3}{10}h$

$$h \leq 2$$

9. Six more than three-fourths a number is greater than or equal to one more than twice the number. Find the number.

$$x \leq -4$$

10. Ms. Garcia wants to carpet her bedroom which requires 24 square yards. Her budget will allow her to spend no more than $600 for the project. If the installation of the carpet will cost $162, what is the most she can pay per square yard for the carpeting?

$18.25 per square yard

Holt Middle School Math

LESSON 10-5 Homework and Practice
Solving for a Variable

Solve each equation for the indicated variable.

1. If the formula of changing Celsius, C, temperature to Fahrenheit, F, temperature is $C = \frac{5}{9} \times (F - 32)$, solve for F.

   $F = \frac{9}{5} \times C + 32$
   _____

2. If the formula for a man's shoe size, s, is $s = 3f - 24$, where f is the foot length in inches, solve for f.

   $\frac{1}{3}s + 8 = f$
   _____

3. If the volume of a cylinder is $V = \pi r^2 h$, where r is the radius of the base and h is the height of the cylinder, solve for h.

   $\frac{V}{\pi r^2} = h$
   _____

Solve each equation for y and graph.

4. $2x + y = 3$

   _____ $y = -2x + 3$ _____

5. $2y - 6x = -8$

   _____ $y = 3x - 4$ _____

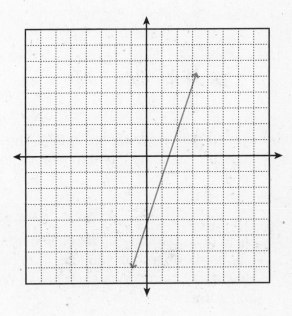

Holt Middle School Math

LESSON 10-6 Homework and Practice
Systems of Equations

Determine if the ordered pair is a solution of each system of equations.

1. $(-1, 3)$
$y = -x + 2$
$y = x + 4$
_____yes_____

2. $(1, 2)$
$y = 2x$
$y - x = 1$
_____yes_____

3. $(3, 5)$
$x - y = 8$
$x + y = -2$
_____no_____

4. $(-1, -4)$
$x = 4y$
$3x + 4y = -4$
_____no_____

5. $(2, 4)$
$3x + 2y = 14$
$2x = y$
_____yes_____

6. $(-2, -8)$
$2x + y = 4$
$3x + y = 2$
_____no_____

7. $(-1, 2)$
$3x + y = 1$
$6x + 2y = -2$
_____no_____

8. $(0, 0)$
$y = 3x - 4$
$y - 3x = -4$
_____no_____

9. $(1, -3)$
$2x = y + 5$
$2x + y = -1$
_____yes_____

Solve each system of equations.

10. $x + y = 12$
$x - y = 0$
_____(6, 6)_____

11. $2x + y = 10$
$x - y = -4$
_____(2, 6)_____

12. $x + y = -8$
$2x - y = -4$
_____(-4, -4)_____

13. $3x + 2y = 0$
$x + 2y = 8$
_____(-4, 6)_____

14. The sum of two numbers is 206. The second number is 48 more than the first. Find the numbers. Write a system of equations and solve.

_____$x + y = 206$; $y = x + 48$; (79,127)_____

15. Ryan and Juan collect baseball cards. Together they have 880 cards. Juan has 125 less than twice as many as Ryan. How many cards does each have? Write a system of equations and solve.

_____$x + y = 880$; $y = 2x - 125$; (335,545); Ryan has 335 cards and Juan has 545 cards._____

Holt Middle School Math

Homework and Practice
LESSON 11-1 *Graphing Linear Equations*

Graph each equation and tell whether it is linear.

1. $y = -3x - 4$

x	−3x − 4	y	(x, y)
−4	−3(−4) − 4	8	(−4, 8)
−3	−3(−3) − 4	5	(−3, 5)
−2	−3(−2) − 4	2	(−2, 2)
−1	−3(−1) − 4	−1	(−1, −1)
0	−3(0) − 4	−4	(0, −4)
1	−3(1) − 4	−7	(1, −7)
2	−3(2) − 4	−10	(2, −10)

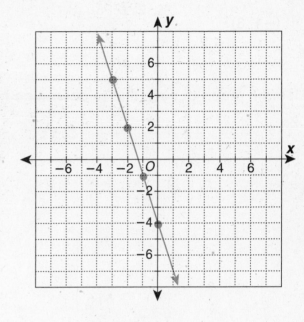

linear

2. $y = x^2 + 2$

x	x² + 2	y	(x, y)
−3	(−3)² + 2	11	(−3, 11)
−2	(−2)² + 2	6	(−2, 6)
−1	(−1)² + 2	3	(−1, 3)
0	(0)² + 2	2	(0, 2)
1	(1)² + 2	3	(1, 3)
2	(2)² + 2	6	(2, 6)
3	(3)² + 2	11	(3, 11)

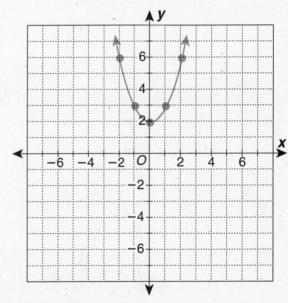

not linear

3. A pharmaceutical representative sells $48,000 in a one month period. The rep earns 5.5% commission plus base salary of $400 a month. How much is the rep paid that month?

$3,040

Holt Middle School Math

Homework and Practice

LESSON 11-2 *Slope of a Line*

Find the slope of the line passing through each pair of points.

1. (5, 7), (6, 9)
2. (2, 8), (8, 2)
3. (−2, 6), (−2, −4)
4. (−8, −7), (−9, −1)

_____2_____ _____−1_____ _____undefined_____ _____−6_____

Use the graph of each line to determine its slope.

5.

_____−4_____

6.

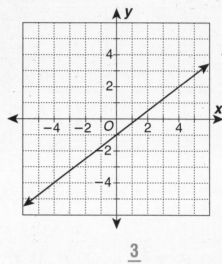

_____$\frac{3}{4}$_____

Tell whether the lines passing through the given points are parallel or perpendicular.

7. line 1: (−1, −2), (−4, −8)
line 2: (−6, 7), (−7, 5)

_____parallel_____

8. line 1: (6, 8), (6, 10)
line 2: (−5, −9), (3, −9)

_____perpendicular_____

9. Graph the line passing through the point (−1, 4) with slope −$\frac{1}{2}$.

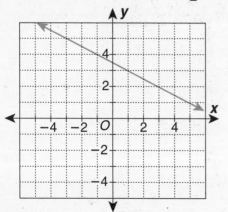

10. Graph the line passing through the point (1, −3) with slope 3.

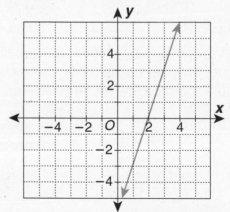

Holt Middle School Math

Name _____ Date _____ Class _____

Find the *x*-intercept and *y*-intercept of each line. Use the intercepts to graph the equation.

1. $x = y + 5$

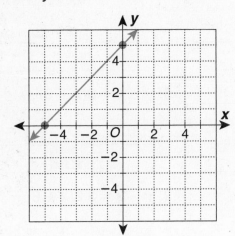

2. $3x - 2y = 6$

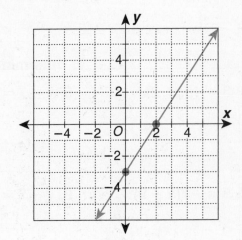

_____
x-intercept is 5;
_____
y-intercept is −5

_____
x-intercept is 2;
_____
y-intercept is −3

Write each equation in slope-intercept form and then find the slope and *y*-intercept.

3. $2x = y - 4$

_____
$y = 2x + 4;$
_____
$m = 2; b = 4$

4. $4x - 3y = -9$

$y = \frac{4}{3}x + 3;$

$m = \frac{4}{3}; b = 3$

5. $x - 4y = 8$

$y = \frac{1}{4}x - 2;$

$m = \frac{1}{4}; b = -2$

Write the equation of the line that passes through each pair of points in slope-intercept form.

6. $(-1, 7), (4, -3)$

_____
$y = -2x + 5$

7. $(2, 5), (-8, 15)$

_____
$y = -x + 7$

8. $(8, 4), (-10, -5)$

$y = \frac{1}{2}x$

9. Thad's father gives him $10 for a passing report card plus $5 for every grade of A. Write an equation of a line in slope-intercept form to express *y*, the amount received with *x* grades of A. State the slope, *x*-intercept, and *y*-intercept of the equation.

_____
$y = 5x + 10; m = 5; b = 10;$ *x*-intercept is −2, *y*-intercept is 10

Holt Middle School Math

Name _____ Date _____ Class _____

Homework and Practice
Point-Slope Form

Identify a point the line passes through and the slope of the line, given the point-slope form of the equation.

1. $y - 6 = 3(x - 2)$

$m = 3; (x_1, y_1) =$
$(2, 6)$

2. $y + 4 = -2(x + 1)$

$m = -2; (x_1, y_1) =$
$(-1, -4)$

3. $y - 5 = -1(x - 8)$

$m = -1; (x_1, y_1) =$
$(8, 5)$

4. $y + 3 = 4(x + 2)$

$m = 4; (x_1, y_1) =$
$(-2, -3)$

5. $y - 7 = -6(x - 1)$

$m = -2; (x_1, y_1) =$
$(1, 7)$

6. $y - 4 = 9(x + 6)$

$m = 9; (x_1, y_1) =$
$(-6, 4)$

7. $y + 5 = -7(x - 9)$

$m = -7; (x_1, y_1) =$
$(9, -5)$

8. $y - 7 = \frac{1}{3}(x + 9)$

$m = \frac{1}{3}; (x_1, y_1) =$
$(-9, 7)$

9. $y - 3 = 3.2(x + 8)$

$m = 3.2; (x_1, y_1) =$
$(-8, 3)$

Write the point-slope form of the equation with the given slope that passes through the indicated point.

10. the line with slope -3 passing through (4, 3)

$y - 3 = -3(x - 4)$

11. the line with slope -1 passing through (6, -2)

$y + 2 = -1(x - 6)$

12. the line with slope 5 passing through (-7, 1)

$y - 1 = 5(x + 7)$

13. the line with slope 7 passing through (-8, -4)

$y + 4 = 7(x + 8)$

14. the line with slope 2 passing through (-9, -6)

$y + 6 = 2(x + 9)$

15. the line with slope -8 passing through (7, -3)

$y + 3 = -8(x - 7)$

16. Write an equation of a line in point-slope form that is parallel to $y = -4x + 7$ and passes through the (8, -5)

$y + 5 = -4(x - 8)$

Holt Middle School Math

Name _____ Date _____ Class _____

Homework and Practice
Direct Variation

Make a graph to determine whether the data set shows direct variation.

1.

x	y
4	3
8	6
0	0
−4	−3

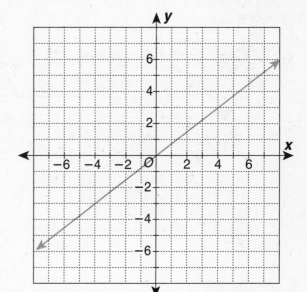

The data set shows a direct

variation.

2. Write the equation of direct variation for exercise 1.

$y = 0.75x$ or $y = \frac{3}{4}x$

Find each equation of direct variation, given that *y* varies directly with *x*.

3. *y* is 27 when *x* is 3

   $y = 9x$

4. *y* is 8 when *x* is −40

   $y = -\frac{1}{5}x$

5. *y* is −54 when *x* is −12

   $y = \frac{9}{2}x$

6. *y* is 21 when *x* is 49

   $y = \frac{3}{7}x$

7. *y* is −31.5 when *x* is 14

   $y = -2.25x$

8. *y* is 180 when *x* is −216

   $y = -\frac{5}{6}x$

9. Bridgett's gross pay per year is $40,300. Her net pay is $27,001 as a result of her payroll deductions. Last year Bridgett's gross salary was $37,700. Her net pay was $25,259. Write an equation of direct variation indicating Bridgett's gross pay, *x*, versus her net pay, *y*.

   $y = 0.67x$

Holt Middle School Math

Homework and Practice

Graphing Inequalities in Two Variables

Graph each inequality.

1. $y \leq 3x - 4$

2. $y + 2x > 5$

3. $x - 3y > 9$

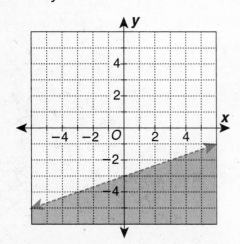

4. $-3x - y \leq 1$

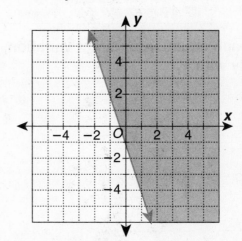

5. Richard must buy clothes for his new job. He has a budget of $250. The shirts he plans on buying cost $15 and the slacks costs $30. Let x equal the number of shirts and y equal the number of pairs of slacks Richard can buy with his clothes allowance. Write an inequality for this information.

$15x + 30y \leq 250$

6. If Richard buys 4 pairs of slacks, what is the most number of shirts he can buy?

The most number of shirts Richard can buy is 8.

Holt Middle School Math

LESSON
11-7

Homework and Practice
Lines of Best Fit

Plot the data and find a line of best fit.

1.

x	2	4	6	8	10	12	14	16
y	12	14	18	16	20	21	25	26

$y = x + 10$

2.

x	5	10	18	20	25	30	35	40
y	135	120	105	90	94	56	50	30

$y = -3x + 150$

3. Nuxhall Company wants to predict their payroll costs for the next
two years based on the salary cost over the past six years. Use
the information in the table below and a line of best fit to
estimate the payroll costs for the next two years.

x	Year 1	Year 2	Year 3	Year 4	Year 5	Year 6
y	$96,750	$104,490	$112,925	$125,150	$131,650	$148,825

Sample: yr 7—$160,731; yr 8—$173,590

Holt Middle School Math

Name _____ Date _____ Class _____

Homework and Practice
Arithmetic Sequences

Determine if each sequence could be arithmetic. If so, give the common difference.

1. −19, −16, −13, −10, −7, …

_____3_____

2. 7, 14, 28, 56, 112, …

_____not_____

3. 8, 1, −6, − 13, − 20, …

_____−7_____

4. 1, 2.2, 4.84, 10.648, 23.4256 …

_____not_____

5. $\frac{1}{10}, \frac{3}{5}, \frac{11}{10}, \frac{8}{5}, \frac{21}{10}, \dots$

_____$\frac{1}{2}$_____

6. −10.4, −8.7, −7.1, −5.4, −3.7, …

_____not_____

7. $\frac{1}{8}, \frac{1}{4}, \frac{3}{8}, \frac{1}{2}, \frac{5}{8}, \dots$

_____$\frac{1}{8}$_____

8. 91, 42, −7, −56, −105, …

_____−49_____

9. −25.3, −18.5, −11.7, −4.9, 1.9, …

_____6.8_____

Find the given term in each arithmetic sequence.

10. 15th term: 35, 42, 49, 56, 63, …

_____133_____

11. 28th term: −41, −29, −17, −5, 7, …

_____283_____

12. 32nd term: 204, 158, 112, 66, 20, …

_____−1,222_____

13. 97th term: −8, −22, −36, −50, −64, …

_____−1,352_____

14. 45th term: 3, 5.9, 8.8, 11.7, 14.6, …

_____130.6_____

15. 61st term: 49, 31, 13, −5, −23, …

_____−1,031_____

16. 74th term: 84, 62, 40, 18, −4, …

_____−1,522_____

17. 37th term: $\frac{1}{9}, \frac{4}{9}, \frac{7}{9}, 1\frac{1}{9}, 1\frac{4}{9}, \dots$

_____$12\frac{1}{9}$_____

18. Write the first six terms in an arithmetic sequence that begins with −8.7 and has a common difference of −3.9.

−8.7, −12.6, −16.5, −20.4, −24.3, −28.2, …

20. Corrine starts a book collection by purchasing seven books. Each week she adds two new books. How many weeks before Corrine has 75 books in her collection?

35 weeks

Holt Middle School Math

Homework and Practice

LESSON 12-2 *Geometric Sequences*

Determine if each sequence could be geometric. If so give the common ratio.

1. 3, 15, 75, 375, 1,875, ...

_____ **5** _____

2. −36, −30, −24, −18, −12, ...

_____ **not** _____

3. 3, $\frac{3}{2}$, $\frac{3}{4}$, $\frac{3}{8}$, $\frac{3}{16}$, ...

_____ $\frac{1}{2}$ _____

4. 850, 170, 34, 6.8, 1.36, ...

_____ **0.2** _____

5. 6, 33, 171, 861, 4,311, ...

_____ **not** _____

6. 14, 98, 686, 4,802, 33,614, ...

_____ **7** _____

7. 999, 333, 111, 99, 33, ...

_____ **not** _____

8. 95, 38, $15\frac{1}{5}$, $6\frac{2}{25}$, $2\frac{54}{125}$, ...

_____ $\frac{2}{5}$ _____

9. 4, 22, 121, 665.5, 3,660.25, ...

_____ **5.5** _____

Find the given term in each geometric sequence. If necessary, round to the nearest hundredth.

10. 8th term; 4, 12, 36, 108, 324, ...

_____ **8,748** _____

11. 5th term; $a_1 = 155$, $r = 0.6$

_____ **20.09** _____

12. 7th term; 4, 14, 49, 171.5, 600.25, ...

_____ **7353.0625** _____

13. 12th term; $a_1 = 0.05$, $r = 9$

_____ **1,569,052,980** _____

14. 16th term; $\frac{1}{3125}$, $\frac{1}{625}$, $\frac{1}{125}$, $\frac{1}{25}$, $\frac{1}{5}$, ...

_____ **9,765,625** _____

15. 9th term; $\frac{7}{9}$, $2\frac{1}{3}$, 7, 21, 63, ...

_____ **5,103** _____

16. Nicholas has a picture that is 3 in. × 5 in. If he enlarges the photo by 25% five times, what are the dimensions of the new photo? Round to the nearest tenth of an inch?

_____ **9.2 in. by 15.3 in.** _____

Holt Middle School Math

Homework and Practice
LESSON 12-3 *Other Sequences*

Use first and second differences to find the next three terms in each sequence.

1. 12, 13, 16, 21, 28, …

___37, 48, 61___

2. 4, 6, 10, 16, 24, …

___34, 46, 60___

3. $\frac{3}{4}$, $2\frac{3}{4}$, $5\frac{1}{4}$, $8\frac{1}{4}$, $11\frac{3}{4}$, …

___$15\frac{3}{4}$, $20\frac{1}{4}$, $25\frac{1}{4}$___

4. 3.6, 4.1, 6.1, 9.6, 14.6, …

___21.1, 29.1, 38.6___

Give the next three terms in each sequence using the simplest rule you can find.

5. 1, 2, 4, 7, 11, …

___16, 22, 29___

6. 6, 7, 10, 15, 22, …

___31, 42, 55___

7. 2, 5, 10, 17, 26, …

___37, 50, 65___

8. 32, 50, 72, 98, 128, …

___162, 200, 242___

9. 400, 361, 324, 289, 256, …

___225, 196, 169___

10. 2.5, 10, 22.5, 40, 62.5, …

___90, 122.5, 160___

Find the first five terms of each sequence defined by the given rule.

11. $a_n = \frac{n^2}{2n}$

$\frac{1}{2}$, 1, $1\frac{1}{2}$, 2, $2\frac{1}{2}$

12. $a_n = \frac{n^2 + 5}{2n}$

3, $2\frac{1}{4}$, $2\frac{1}{3}$, $2\frac{5}{8}$, 3

13. $a_n = \frac{6n - 2}{n^2 + 1}$

2, 2, $1\frac{3}{5}$, $1\frac{5}{17}$, $1\frac{1}{13}$

14. Suppose *a, b,* and *c* are three consecutive numbers in the Fibonacci sequence. Complete the following table and guess the pattern.

___The result of b^2 is one less than___

___the product of *a* and *c.*___

a, b, c	ac	b^2
1, 1, 2	2	1
2, 3, 5	10	9
5, 8, 13	65	64
13, 21, 34	442	441
34, 55, 89	3,026	3,025

Holt Middle School Math

LESSON 12-4 Homework and Practice
Functions

Complete the table and graph each function.

1. $y = 3x + 4$

x	3x + 4	y
−3	3(−3) + 4	−5
−2	3(−2) + 4	−2
−1	3(−1) + 4	1
0	3(0) + 4	4
1	3(1) + 4	7

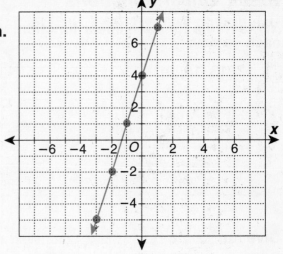

2. $y = 2x^2 - 1$

x	2x² − 1	y
−2	2(−2)² − 1	7
−1	2(−1)² − 1	1
0	2(0)² − 1	−1
1	2(1)² − 1	1
2	2(2)² − 1	7

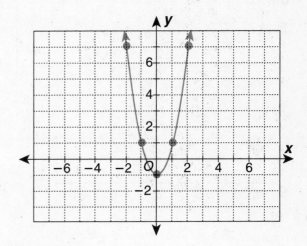

Determine if each relationship represents a function.

3. $y^2 = 4x - 3$

_____no_____

4.

x	2	4	6	8
y	−1	−2	−3	−4

_____yes_____

5. For each function, find $f(0)$, $f(-1)$, and $f(2)$.

Function	f (0)	f (−1)	f (2)
$y = -5x + 2$	2	7	−8
$y = 3x^2 - 8$	−8	−5	4

6. Given the function $f(x) = -4x^2 - 5$ and the domain
{ −3, −2, −1, 0, 1, 2, 3 }. Find the range of the function.

range is { −41, −21, −9, −5 }

Holt Middle School Math

LESSON 12-5 Homework and Practice
Linear Functions

Write a rule for each linear function.

1.

$f(x) = 2x + 5$

2.
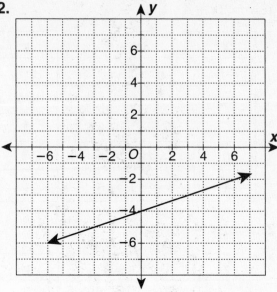

$f(x) = \frac{1}{3}x - 4$

3.

x	−4	−2	3	5
f(x)	13	7	−8	−14

$f(x) = -3x + 1$

4.

x	−6	−4	2	8
f(x)	−10	−9	−6	−3

$f(x) = \frac{1}{2}x - 7$

5. A salesperson is paid a base salary of $300 plus 8% of their sales. Write a function rule for the salary. Graph the function.

$f(x) = 0.08x + 300$

6. If a salesperson has $900 in sales, what is the salesperson's salary?

$372

96

Holt Middle School Math

LESSON 12-6 Homework and Practice
Exponential Functions

Create a table for each exponential function, and use it to graph the function.

1. $f(x) = 0.25 \cdot 5^x$

x	y
−1	$y = 0.25 \cdot 5^{-1} = 0.05$
0	$y = 0.25 \cdot 5^0 = 0.25$
1	$y = 0.25 \cdot 5^1 = 1.25$
2	$y = 0.25 \cdot 5^2 = 6.25$

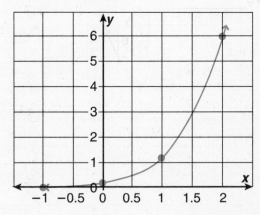

2. $f(x) = \frac{1}{4} \cdot 6^x$

x	y
−1	$y = \frac{1}{4} \cdot 6^{-1} = \frac{1}{24}$
0	$y = \frac{1}{4} \cdot 6^0 = \frac{1}{4}$
1	$y = \frac{1}{4} \cdot 6^1 = 1\frac{1}{2}$
2	$y = \frac{1}{4} \cdot 6^2 = 9$

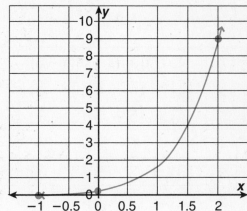

3. A lawyer opens a new office with 28 clients. She intends to increase her clientele 30% each year for the next 4 years. How many clients can she expect to have at the end of 4 years? Round the answer to the nearest whole number?

80 clients

4. A company owns office cars worth a total of $587,000. The cars are depreciated by 12% a year for 10 years. What is the expected value of the cars at the end of 10 years? Round the answer to the nearest cent.

$163,480.07

5. Clayton earns $725 a week at his job. He is given a 6% annual increase in pay. How much will Clayton earn per week after 3 years? Round the answer to the nearest cent.

$863.49

Holt Middle School Math

Homework and Practice

Quadratic Functions

Create a table for each quadratic function and use it to make a graph.

1. $f(x) = x^2 - 6$

x	$f(x) = x^2 - 6$
-3	$f(-3) = (-3)^2 - 6 = 3$
-1	$f(-1) = (-1)^2 - 6 = -5$
0	$f(0) = (0)^2 - 6 = -6$
2	$f(2) = (2)^2 - 6 = -2$
3	$f(3) = (3)^2 - 6 = 3$

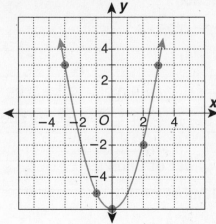

2. $f(x) = (x - 5)(x - 3)$

x	$f(x) = (x - 5)(x - 3)$
6	$f(5) = (6 - 5)(6 - 3) = 3$
5	$f(5) = (5 - 5)(5 - 3) = 0$
4	$f(4) = (4 - 5)(4 - 3) = -1$
3	$f(3) = (3 - 5)(3 - 3) = 0$
2	$f(2) = (2 - 5)(2 - 3) = 3$

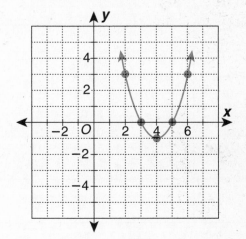

3. $f(x) = x^2 - 3x - 2$

x	$f(x) = x^2 - 3x - 2$
3	$f(3) = (3)^2 - 3(3) - 2 = -2$
2	$f(2) = (2)^2 - 3(2) - 2 = -4$
1	$f(1) = (1)^2 - 3(1) - 2 = -4$
0	$f(0) = (0)^2 - 3(0) - 2 = -2$
-1	$f(-1) = (-1)^2 - 3(-1) - 2 = 2$

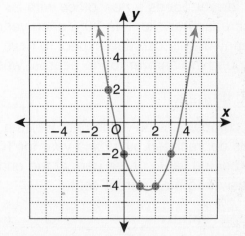

4. If the perimeter of a rectangle is 124 cm, find the dimensions of the rectangle with the greatest possible area? What is the greatest possible area?

31 cm × 31 cm; area = 961 cm^2

Holt Middle School Math

Homework and Practice

Inverse Variation

Tell whether each relationship is an inverse variation.

1. The table shows the length and width of a parallelogram.

Length	4	8	10	12	36
Width	18	9	7.2	6	2

The relationship is an inverse variation.

2. The table shows the number of shelves and the number of books on each shelf in a library. $y = \dfrac{72}{x}$

Number of Shelves	3	4	6	12	16
Number of Books	32	24	16	8	6

The relationship is an inverse variation.

3. The table shows the number of guests at a party and the cost per guest. $y = \dfrac{96}{x}$

Number of Guests	66	75	96	100	150
Cost per Guest	9	8	6.25	6	4

The relationship is not an inverse variation.

Graph each inverse variation.

4. $f(x) = \dfrac{6}{x}$

5. $f(x) = \dfrac{-4}{x}$

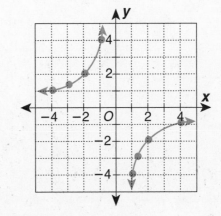

6. Hertz, abbreviated Hz, is a unit of frequency equal to 1 cycle per second. The pitch of a musical instrument is measured in vibrations per second or Hertz. If the pitch of a panpipe 2 feet long is 282 Hz, what is the length of pipe with a pitch of 376 Hz?

1.5 feet

Holt Middle School Math